D1327984

Guide to Fossil Man

A Handbook of Human Palaeontology

BY MICHAEL H. DAY

Senior Lecturer in Anatomy
The Middlesex Hospital Medical School
University of London

Hon. Associate
Unit of Primatology and Human Evolution
Royal Free Hospital School of Medicine
University of London

With a Foreword by
PROFESSOR J. S. WEINER

CASSELL : LONDON

CASSELL & COMPANY LTD
35 Red Lion Square, London W C I
Melbourne, Sydney, Toronto
Johannesburg, Cape Town, Auckland

Printed in Great Britain by
The Camelot Press Ltd, London and Southampton

Foreword

What were our ancestors really like? How far back can we trace
them? Can we discern in the fossil record a continuous sequence of
transformation? Questions such as these constitute tests of the
theory of evolution as applied to mankind, or more particularly
whether the palaeontological record supports the belief that natural
selection (interacting on genetic recombination and mutation and
such factors as isolation and hybridization) must have been at work
in bringing about the emergence of modern man from some remote
ape-like stock. These questions Darwin could not answer positively
simply because the fossil material was almost totally deficient in his
day. Nevertheless, so firmly based did he consider his theory of
evolution that in the *Descent of Man* (published twelve years after
the *Origin*) he made 'predictions' about the earlier stages of human
evolution. The remarkable accuracy of his reconstructions has
not perhaps been fully appreciated. Darwin did in fact depict the
main features of the two stages which nowadays we should see as
corresponding to the *Dryopithecus* level (roughly 20 million years
ago) and the *Australopithecine* level (roughly $1\frac{1}{2}$ million years ago).

A paramount requirement for the student of evolution is of
course a thorough grasp of general evolutionary theory and
evolutionary genetics aided by an understanding of taxonomic
principles and particularly of the statistical methods for assessing
degrees of affinity. At the same time the student of human
evolution must obviously possess a detailed acquaintance with the
fossil material available. This requirement is extremely well served
by this handbook prepared by Dr Michael Day. The great majority
of students will never be able to see complete collections of casts of
the fossil material. This book provides, in a convenient way, a
sufficiently detailed insight to all the important fossil material
bearing on human evolution. Dr Day has provided a judicious
coverage, both in his descriptive text and in the accompanying
photographs, of all the fossil material of key importance for
evolutionary interpretation. He has also given essential ancillary
information about the locations of the finds and probable dating
along with climatic and faunal particulars.

The material assembled by Dr Day reveals both the fascination
and difficulties of this subject. From his careful descriptions it will
be seen at once that the many fossil 'men' we talk about, so far

from being whole skeletons, are very sadly incomplete. Most are without trunk or limbs, many are faceless and not a few are represented merely by a mandible and teeth. Compared to what was available, even only thirty years ago, the material in bulk is undoubtedly quite impressive, but the serious palaeontological student should never forget how fragmentary many of the individual 'key' finds really are. He must bear this fact always in mind so as not to slip into the temptation of creating some idealized version of the actual material. Many of the weaknesses (and unnecessary controversies) of human palaeontology are derived from this all-too-human propensity. For anyone who wishes to be properly informed on the limitations of the available material I strongly recommend that he keep Dr Day's book constantly to hand.

J. S. Weiner
Past President
Royal Anthropological Institute

Contents

List of Illustrations

Introduction

The study of human evolution presents many problems of peculiar difficulty, perhaps the greatest being the large and increasing number of specimens forming the evidence upon which the subject is based. In this book an attempt has been made to select, from the wide range of known material, the hominid fossils that best illustrate a significant stage or aspect of human palaeontology, the study of fossil man.

Anatomical examination of fossil bones and teeth can be revealing, tantalizing, exasperating. Always the temptation is to speculate beyond the facts, to argue from the particular to the general, to forget that one specimen represents a population and is therefore subject to the laws of biological variation. However, if these pitfalls are avoided, there remains an ever increasing body of knowledge of the anatomy of fossil man. Even so, anatomical knowledge is not enough upon which to base an assessment of the life of early man; other factors must be considered, the climate, the time relationships of different groups and the culture of the populations represented by the scant remains at our disposal.

It is the purpose of this book to bring together information from many disciplines and relate it for each of the 40 or so key sites which have yielded the bulk of significant hominid fossils.

Acknowledgments

It is with pleasure that I record my thanks to the many people who have assisted me during the preparation of this book. I am particularly grateful to Professor E. W. Walls who has generously put at my disposal the facilities of the Anatomy Department of The Middlesex Hospital Medical School; in addition he has patiently read the text and suggested many improvements which have been incorporated. Similarly I am grateful to Dr J. R. Napier and his assistants of the Unit of Primatology and Human Evolution, Royal Free Hospital School of Medicine, for their advice and helpful criticism. In this respect I must specially thank Alan Walker for his kindness in advising me in the many fields in which he has special knowledge.

For the opportunity to examine original material, the provision of photographs and for helpful discussion I am indebted to many; but I must mention Dr K. P. Oakley, Professor J. S. Weiner, Dr L. S. B. Leakey, Professor P. V. Tobias, Dr G. H. R. von Koenigswald, Dr D. A. Hooijer, Professor J. T. Robinson, Professor C. Arambourg, Dr A. T. Sutcliffe, D. R. Brothwell, Dr R. Kraatz, Professor F. Twiesselmann, Dr C. K. Brain, Dr A. Rosenfeld, the Director of the Musée de l'Homme, Paris, and the Trustees of the British Museum.

I must also draw attention to the kindness of the Librarians of the Middlesex Hospital Medical School, the Royal Anthropological Institute and the British Museum (Natural History). The text-figures and maps reflect the skill of Mrs Audrey Besterman.

PART I

The Pleistocene Period

All the known remains of fossil man have been attributed to deposits formed within the Pleistocene period which is taken as extending from one and a half million years ago to the Recent or Holocene period, say the last 10,000–8,000 years. In relation to the total span of geological time the Pleistocene and Holocene periods are short, for the first recognizable fossil animal forms have been dated at *c.* 600 million years B.P. (Before the Present). Seemingly, the evolutionary changes that transformed the early hominids into modern man occurred within a relatively brief period, and the inference must follow that during this time selective pressures on the hominids were high, and that only those forms able to adapt to rapidly changing conditions would be likely to survive.

There is little doubt that the environment was unstable during the Pleistocene period; arctic conditions spread from the poles on several occasions producing ice sheets and glaciers in Northern Europe, Asia, North America, the Antarctic, and in mountainous regions such as the Himalayas and the Alps. Alternating with these glacial periods were warmer phases (interglacials) when the climate was warm/temperate or even tropical in parts of Europe. During the glacial periods the sea level was much lower than at present as much of the world's water was piled up on land as snow and ice, so allowing Britain to be joined to the continent of Europe, and many of the islands of South-east Asia to the neighbouring mainland: but with the return of warmer conditions the pent-up snow and ice flowed back to the sea and the shore line was raised.

Further evidence that these climatic fluctuations were world-wide derives from parts of Africa where Pleistocene lake deposits bear witness to alternating wetter and drier phases (pluvials and interpluvials) that may be correlated with the glacial phases—of high snowfall—and interglacials in Europe.

The effects of the alternations of cold and warm phases upon the sea level of the Mediterranean have been provisionally correlated with Alpine glacial and interglacial phases (Table 1).

Investigation of the deposits laid down during the Pleistocene period has taken place in many parts of the world; as a result the local sequence of glacial and interglacial conditions has been established. Correlations between regional sequences are probably valid on a broad basis if the

3

Table 1   Sea Level Changes During the Pleistocene Period Phases

Alpine Glacial and Interglacial Phases	Rise in Sea Level	Fall in Sea Level
Late Würm Interstadial to final Post-Glacial	Versilian	—
MAIN WÜRM GLACIATION	—	Pre-Versilian
Early Würm Interstadial	Late Monastirian (= Tyrrhenian III)	—
WÜRM I GLACIATION	—	Inter-Monastirian
Riss–Würm Interglacial	Main Monastirian (= Tyrrhenian II)	—
RISS GLACIATION	—	Pre-Monastirian
Mindel–Riss Interglacial	Tyrrhenian I	—
MINDEL II GLACIATION	—	Romanian (Pre-Tyrrhenian)
Mindel I/II Interstadial	Sicilian II (Milazzian)	—
MINDEL I GLACIATION	—	Inter-Sicilian
Günz–Mindel Interglacial	Sicilian I	—
GÜNZ GLACIATION	—	Pre-Sicilian
Donau–Günz Interstadial	Calabrian	—
DONAU GLACIATION	—	Post-Astian

(AFTER OAKLEY, 1964)

localities concerned are not too far apart; world-wide correlations of glacial/interglacial or pluvial/interpluvial phases are less securely founded.

One result of the difficulties of inter-regional correlation has been the multiplication of terms. The table above gives the approximate correlations of glacial and interglacial terminology.

The Geology of Fossil Sites

It is a well-known palaeontological aphorism that the distribution of fossils tends to equate with the distribution of collectors. Although this is partly true the chances of animal bones becoming fossilized will depend primarily upon the place and the circumstances of its life and death. If the bones are not destroyed by scavengers their preservation will be subject to the nature of the deposit in which they become buried. Bone consists of organic matter and mineral salts; the mineral substance forms about 66 per cent of the weight of a bone and is made   4

Table 2   The Pleistocene Glacial and Interglacial Periods (Probable equivalents)

Alpine Terms	Numerical Terms	English Terms	European Terms	American Terms	General Terms (Zeuner)	Pleistocene	YEARS B.P. (Not to Scale)
WÜRM III GLACIATION	Fourth Glaciation			Late Wisconsin Glaciation	Last Glaciation	UPPER PLEISTOCENE	10,000
WÜRM II/III INTERSTADIAL			Paudorf Interstadial				24,000
WÜRM II GLACIATION		—	Weichselian Glaciation	Port Talbot Interstadial			27,000
WÜRM I/II INTERSTADIAL			Gottweiger or First Interstadial				32,000
WÜRM I GLACIATION				Early Wisconsin Glaciation			45,000
RISS–WÜRM INTERGLACIAL	Third Interglacial	Ipswichian Interglacial	Eemian Interglacial	Sangamon Interglacial	Last Interglacial		70,000
RISS GLACIATION	Third Glaciation	—	Saalian Glaciation	Illinoian Glaciation	Penultimate Glaciation		c. 150,000
MINDEL–RISS INTERGLACIAL	Second Interglacial	Hoxnian Interglacial (Great Interglacial)	Holsteinian Interglacial	Yarmouth Interglacial	Penultimate Interglacial		c. 200,000
MINDEL GLACIATION	Second Glaciation	—	Elsterian Glaciation	Kansan Glaciation	Antepenultimate Glaciation	MIDDLE PLEISTOCENE	c. 300,000
GÜNZ–MINDEL INTERGLACIAL	First Interglacial	Cromerian Interglacial	—	Aftonian Interglacial	Antepenultimate Interglacial		c. 400,000
GÜNZ GLACIATION	First Glaciation	—	Taxandrian Glaciation	Nebraskan Glaciation	Early Glaciation	LOWER PLEISTOCENE (VILLAFRANCHIAN)	c. 1,000,000
DONAU–GÜNZ INTERGLACIAL	—	—	Tiglian Interglacial	—	—		
DONAU GLACIATION	—	—	Praetiglian Glaciation	—	—		

Plio-Pleistocene Boundary, c. 1,500,000

up of calcium phosphate and calcium carbonate with traces of calcium fluoride, magnesium carbonate and sodium chloride. Burial in an acid deposit, such as a forest floor, will lead to rapid bacterial putrefaction and disintegration of the bones. On the other hand burial in an alkaline deposit, with protection from bacteria, will encourage preservation.

It is not surprising, therefore, that the majority of hominid fossil sites are in limestone caves, alkaline volcanic material or lake and river sediments.

CAVE DEPOSITS

Cave fillings frequently consist of bone breccia, a consolidated rock containing angular fragments of rock and fossil bones embedded in a cement material. If the cave has been occupied by hominids, layers of deposits may accumulate containing animal bones, stone tools and other artefacts, fragments from the roof and perhaps ash from a fire. These layers constitute recognizable living floors and provide important evidence of the sequence of occupation.

VOLCANIC DEPOSITS

Bone preservation is particularly good in deposits of fine-grained volcanic material, whether of wind-blown ash or volcanic material that has settled in still water. Minor fluctuations in the level of shallow lakes in areas of volcanic activity may result in the covering of bones over a wide area near the lakeside.

RIVER DEPOSITS

Water-laid gravels and sands are often deposited by rivers that are in process of aggrading the material they are carrying. Such material is derived from a site of erosion upstream and may contain fossil bones that have been carried some distance and redeposited. Many such bones show signs of water-rolling and may be derived from older deposits. None the less river deposits are important field sites because remains from a wide area will be concentrated by the tributaries of the main stream.

It is essential when fossil bones are discovered that every effort is made to record accurately the precise site and circumstances of the find. Once a specimen has been removed it may be impossible to determine exactly its relationship to the deposit in which it was found.

Stone Tools

A cultural criterion which has been used to define the human level of hominid evolutionary advancement is the ability to conceive a use for an implement, and to select and modify a natural object for this   6 purpose. When this is done repeatedly and in a regular fashion a cultural tradition or industry is established.

Whatever objects were used by early man, those most likely to survive as traces of his workmanship would be those made from stone. Once it was realized that primitive man had made stone tools and weapons, large numbers of artefacts have been identified and classified in order of increasing craftsmanship and diversity of purpose.

To the untrained eye one stone may look much like another, but often certain diagnostic features can be discerned which will determine whether a stone has been deliberately fashioned or not. Not all rocks are suitable for tool-making, but amongst those which have been employed are flint, obsidian, chert, quartzite and other glass-like substances capable of taking an edge.

When a flint is deliberately struck, the point of impact forms the apex of a cone when the nodule shatters. If the blow is directed at the edge of the nodule, a flake may be struck off bearing a half cone, or bulb of percussion; the parent nodule will retain a negative impression, or negative bulb. The morphology of the flake or its core may be altered by shaping the outline to form a blade, axe-head or scraper, and the edge may be sharpened by retouching with delicate blows. Analysis of the methods of manufacture of flint implements has given the prehistorian criteria whereby to distinguish between cultural traditions.

Clearly, since a pebble dashed on a beach may fortuitously show a bulb of percussion, it is important to take the situation of the find into careful account. Again, should a rock be foreign to the site at which it was found, its transportation must be explained; if no geological explanation is feasible, then human agency can be considered.

Broadly, stone tools may be classified as follows:

EARLY PALAEOLITHIC TOOLS

Pebble tools are simply flaked in one or two directions to produce a crude cutting or scraping implement (Oldowan culture).

Hand-axes have the flaking process continued crudely all round the stone to produce a biface with an irregular border (Chellean; Abbevillian). Later hand-axes are pointed, ovate or almond shaped, the flaking more delicate and the edge straighter (Acheulean).

Chopper tools are coarse, crudely made implements, either flakes or cores, showing little sign of craftsmanship (Choukoutienian and Soan).

Flake tools of a simple type may occur in pebble industries, but a well defined early flake culture is known from Europe. The tools were derived from cores and there is evidence that the edges were retouched (Clactonian; Tayacian).

Later the flake cultures improved when the technique of striking a flake from a carefully prepared 'tortoise-core' was evolved. Such a flake may show a bulb of percussion and need little or no retouching (Levalloisian).

An industry characteristically associated with Neanderthal man consists of a combination of hand-axes and flake tools. Typical implements of this industry are pointed scrapers, triangular knife blades, hammer stones and small hand-axes (Mousterian).

LATE PALAEOLITHIC TOOLS

Blade Tools and Burins dominate the later phases of the Old Stone Age. The blades are straight-edged and backed by a blunted border, whilst the burin is an engraving tool bearing a variety of shaped working points (Chattelperonian; Aurignacian; Perigordian). This type of culture was finally expressed in the beautiful leaf-shaped blades and points made by a 'pressure flaking' technique (Solutrean). It is from the Late Palaeolithic, in particular the Magdalenian phase, that the first evidence of worked bone, ivory and antlers derived; spear points, harpoons and bone needles have been found as well as signs that stone tools were hafted. The people responsible for the Aurignacian and Magdalenian cultures have also left remarkable traces of their skill in the form of cave painting and sculpture.

MESOLITHIC AND NEOLITHIC TOOLS

Cultural advance was now rapid and led to the use of small flakes (microliths) set in wooden handles for spear points and harpoons, barbed points and arrow-heads. Later, polished stone axe-heads typify the Neolithic phase of cultural advance which included early agriculture and the domestication of animals.

Dating Fossil Man

It is obviously of the greatest importance that the remains of fossil man should be correctly placed within the time sequence of the Pleistocene and Holocene periods; firstly, so that morphological evidence from

Fig. 1   Lower Palaeolithic stone tools
1. Oldowan implement, Bed 1, Olduvai Gorge, Tanzania, East Africa
2. Choukoutienian chopper tool, Lower Cave, Peking, Peoples' Republic of China
3. Acheulean lanceolate hand-axe or ficron, Swanscombe, Kent
4. Clactonian flake tool, Swanscombe, Kent
5. Acheulean hand-axe, Swanscombe, Kent

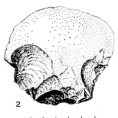

1

2

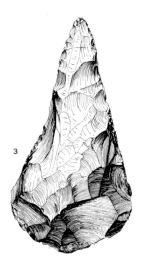

3

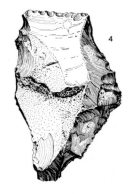

4

5

the bones can be interpreted in terms of hominid phylogeny, and secondly, so that ecological information from the sites can be correlated with the hominid remains. Rigorous dating methods can also eliminate from consideration such 'fossils' as the Galley Hill skeleton and Piltdown man.

When considering the age of a fossil specimen, two questions must be answered:

1. What is its relationship to the geological, faunal and archaeological sequence at the site?
2. What is its chronological age in years B.P.?

The answer to the first question will tell whether the remains are contemporaneous with the deposit in which they were found, and therefore if the faunal, climatic and archaeological information derived from the deposit can properly be associated with the find; in brief its Relative Age can be assessed.

The answer to the second question will provide a figure—its Absolute—or Chronometric Age.

CONTEMPORANEITY

In order to establish the contemporaneity of a particular fossil bone with the deposit in which it was found, evidence must be shown by the field worker that the deposit has not been unnaturally disturbed, and that no possibility exists of intrusive burial or derivation from older deposits. Photographs of the site with the specimen *in situ*, accompanied by stratigraphic drawings, giving the exact location of the find are

Fig. 2   Middle and Upper Palaeolithic, and Neolithic stone tools

    6. Levalloisian flake tool, Baker's Hole, Kent
          Drawn by courtesy of the Trustees of the British Museum
    7. Mousterian side scraper
    8. Mousterian point, Le Moustier, Dordogne, France
    9. Gravettian backed blade, Les Roches, Sergeac, Dordogne, France
          Drawn by courtesy of the Trustees of the British Museum
   10. Solutrean laurel-leaf blade, Solutré, Dordogne, France
          Drawn by courtesy of the Trustees of the British Museum
   11. Magdalenian end scraper, La Madelaine, Dordogne, France
          Drawn by courtesy of the Trustees of the British Museum
   12. Magdalenian burin, Dordogne, France
   13. (*a*) Lunate microlith, Brakfontein, Cape Province, Republic of South Africa
          (*b*) British Neolithic leaf-shaped arrowhead
          (*c*) Neolithic tanged and barbed arrowhead, Fayum, Egypt
   14. Neolithic polished flint axe-head, Thames Valley

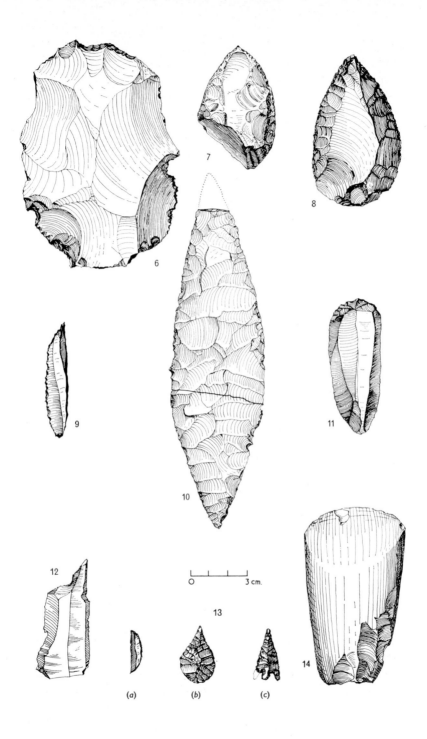

6

7

8

9

10

11

12

13

(a)   (b)   (c)

14

0   3 cm.

essential. If these conditions are satisfied two chemical methods are applicable, provided that other fossil bones are recovered from the same deposit.

It is known that fluorine tends to accumulate in buried bone, under certain conditions, at a rate determined by its local concentration in the soil and the length of burial. In this way it may be possible to show that hominid bones are contemporaneous with the bones of extinct mammals in the deposit. Similarly it is known that nitrogen tends to decrease in buried bone, thus nitrogen estimations can be used for the same purpose. Unfortunately nitrogen tends to disappear rapidly under oxidizing conditions and may be absent altogether.

RELATIVE DATING

If the contemporaneity of the specimen bone and its deposit is established, a great deal more information may become available. The geology of the region may be identifiable by comparison with other known sections; the pollen content of the deposit may be investigated and correlated; the fossil faunal assemblage may be compared with that of other sites and different layers of the same site; stone tools may be recognized and similarly compared. In this way information about the environment of the specimen form is gradually pieced together and its relative position in the geological, climatic, faunal and archaeological sequence is established.

ABSOLUTE DATING

Only one direct method of absolute dating is in common use. Nitrogen in the upper atmosphere is bombarded by neutrons produced by cosmic radiation; this results in the formation of a known proportion of radioactive carbon which becomes incorporated in carbon dioxide. This is absorbed by vegetation and thence passes into animal tissues. When bones are buried the radioactive carbon (C 14) begins to decay at a known rate. Measurements of the carbon 14 content of buried organic matter can be translated mathematically to give an estimate of the age of the specimen. In practice the method is limited to material less than 60–70,000 years old since above this age the amount of carbon 14 remaining is too small to estimate.

Another radiometric method (the potassium–argon technique) depends upon the fact that naturally occurring potassium contains a radioactive isotope; this isotope decays at a constant rate producing argon which is held within the crystals of some potassic minerals. Estimates of the argon content of a sample of these minerals, derived from a deposit containing fossil bones, will indirectly measure the age of the bones. Clearly the contemporaneity of the bones and the deposit

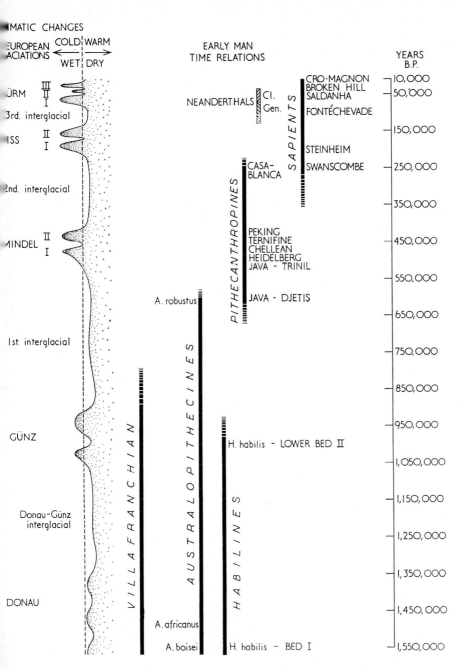

Fig. 3   Fossil hominids and the Pleistocene period

must be established beyond doubt before the result is acceptable. In practice use of the method is limited to deposits containing potassic minerals not less than 20,000 years old.

Recently a new method of chronometric dating has been introduced in which past climatic changes, as shown by variations in the biological and radiochemical constituents of deep-sea cores, are matched against climatic changes deduced from land deposits. Once again the contemporaneity of a specimen and its deposit must be established, but in addition accurate correlation between sea bed changes and land changes must be achieved before the results of this method are acceptable.

The relative dating of a specimen, whose contemporaneity is beyond doubt, can sometimes be established by agreement of results from several disciplines such as geology, palaeontology, archaeology and palynology. In this event it is likely that its chronometric age can be inferred by reference to the increasing number of well established dates within the Pleistocene period.

The approximate time relationships of early man and the major climatic changes in the Pleistocene period are shown in Fig. 3.

References and Further Reading

BISHOP, W. W. 1964 'The later Tertiary and Pleistocene in Eastern and Equatorial Africa'. In *African ecology and human evolution*. Eds. F. C. Howell and F. Bourlière, pp. 246-275. London: Methuen and Co. Ltd.

FLINT, R. F. 1957 *Glacial and Pleistocene geology*. 2nd Ed. New York: Wiley.

OAKLEY, K. P. and MUIR-WOOD, H. 1962 *The succession of life through geological time*. 4th Ed. London: British Museum (Natural History).

OAKLEY, K. P. 1963 *Man the tool-maker*. 6th Ed. London: British Museum (Natural History).

OAKLEY, K. P. 1964 *Frameworks for dating fossil man*. London: Weidenfeld and Nicholson.

ZEUNER, F. E. 1958 *Dating the past*. 4th Ed. Revised. London: Methuen and Co. Ltd.

ZEUNER, F. E. 1959 *The Pleistocene period*. London: Hutchinson and Co. Ltd.

PART II

The principal evidence upon which knowledge of the evolution of man rests has been provided by anatomical examination of fossil bones and teeth. Although skeletal and dental structure may appear limited sources of information, behavioural characteristics—such as loco-motor capability and dietary habit—may be deducible from their study.

In the past, emphasis was placed upon the phyletic value of single features whose functional significance was often obscure, for example, the variations in the arrangement of skull sutures. How-ever, wider knowledge of the range of variation of single features in all primates has allowed these characteristics to be regarded in proper perspective.

The study of individual bones is of greater value, and an analysis of joint geometry and muscular mechanics can often strongly infer joint function. When there is available a group of bones that form a func-tional complex (hand, foot, pelvis, vertebral column, jaws and teeth) its examination will give the beginnings of an insight into the life of the form of which it once formed part. Also, with sufficient material, knowledge of several functional complexes may be built up to provide almost the entire picture, morphological and functional; such a process, however, must stop short of modelling soft tissue features and hair distribution, for which no direct evidence exists.

Bones

It is apparent that the study of fossil man requires a working knowledge of the skeleton of modern man; the terminology of human palaeonto-logy closely parallels that of human osteology, but it is not within the scope of this book to describe the human skeleton, a topic dealt with in all standard anatomical texts. However, perhaps certain aspects of osteology acquire importance when set against a comparative back-ground, and thus deserve emphasis.

Bone is living tissue, if it is cut, it bleeds; if broken, it heals. As with other living tissue, it reacts to stimuli; in particular it responds to mechanical stresses, a principle embodied in Wolff's Law:

'The external form and internal architecture of a bone are related to the forces which act upon it.'

It follows that the shape of a bone, although genetically determined,   17 is capable of modification, and at death the external form and internal architecture will reflect the work that it was called upon to perform during the latter part of life. It is upon this premise that much of the interpretation of skeletal morphology depends.

NORMAL SKELETAL VARIATION

It is a commonplace that no two people are alike; neither are their skeletons nor the individual bones and teeth of which they are composed. Every morphological feature and every measurement forms but a part of the range of normal biological variation to be found within a population. Sampling techniques can be employed to define the approximate limits of this range and the distribution of characteristics within it. While statistical methods can assist in the evaluation of observations and in the comparison of data, unfortunately hominid fossil bones and teeth are frequently too few in number to allow proper statistical comparisons between them and samples drawn from populations of related forms. Often the most that can be achieved is to determine whether or not a given character (which may itself be at any point within its own range of normal variation) lies within the range of normal variation of that character in an allied form.

In order to facilitate comparison, indices can be devised which allow two variables to be expressed as a single figure; length in terms of breadth (crania, tooth crowns), shaft thickness in terms of length (long bones). Comparison of indices allows specimens of differing absolute sizes to be compared in respect of a relative feature. Occasionally more sophisticated techniques such as multivariate analysis may be appropriate.

SEXUAL VARIATION

Sexual dimorphism is often regarded as a common feature of the skeletons of the hominids including modern man, and on this account it is frequently taken for granted that a large robust bone is male whereas a small gracile bone is female. A moment's reflection should suffice to establish that this is not an invariable rule in modern man. What is probably true is that the means of the ranges of normal skeletal size variation of male and female hominids are separated, the male being the higher; however, this gives no firm basis for asserting the sex of any individual unknown hominid bone, fossil or recent, on the grounds of size.

The only sexual characters upon which some reliance may be placed are the morphological features of the pelvis; it is well known in modern man that these will assist in differentiating male from female pelves (see Table 3).

Table 3   The Principal Differences between the Modern Human Male and Female Pelvis

MALE PELVIS	FEMALE PELVIS
1. Sacrum straight and upright	Sacrum hollowed and forward tilted
2. Inferior pubic ramus strongly everted	Inferior pubic ramus weakly everted
3. Sciatic notch 90° or less	Sciatic notch 90° or more
4. Inferior pubic angle 90° or less	Inferior pubic angle 90° or more
5. Length of superior pubic ramus equals acetabular diameter	Length of superior pubic ramus is greater than acetabular diameter
6. The ilia are upstanding	The ilia are flattened
7. The ischial spines are prominent and project inwards	The ischial spines are not prominent and do not project inwards

None of the characters listed above is diagnostic on its own, but taken in conjunction with each other they provide some evidence upon which to base an opinion.

AGE VARIATION

Growing Phase. Age changes in bones are well recognized during the period of skeletal development. Long bones ossify from centres which appear early in intra-uterine development near the mid-point of the cartilage pre-cursor of the shaft. The ossification process spreads from this diaphysial centre towards the ends of the bone; later new epiphysial centres appear at the ends. The cartilage plate separating the diaphysis from the epiphysis constitutes the growing zone. Additional bone is laid down beneath the periosteum which surrounds the shaft. Remodelling, by resorption and addition, modifies the structure until development is nearly complete, then the epiphysis fuses on to the shaft and the bone is adult.

The state of skeletal maturity allows some estimate to be made of age, although variability is common between individuals and between species. It is probably unwise to make estimates of the chronological age at death of an immature fossil bone on the basis of correlation with similar bones of modern man, other than in broad categories such as foetal, infant, juvenile and adolescent.

Mature Phase. During adult life age changes are comparatively few. Tooth attrition is continuous, but its rate is influenced by diet and the state of dental health. Typically, adult fossil hominid incisors are worn down so that in occlusion the bite is 'edge to edge'.

Skeletal changes during adult life include the gradual obliteration of   19

Table 4   *Modern Human Post-Cranial Skeletal Maturation (Long bones)*

Bone	Appearance of Centres Diaphysis	Epiphysis	Fusion of Diaphysis and Epiphysis
Clavicle	5–6/52 intra-uterine life (i.u.)	15–17 years	21 years
Humerus	8/52 i.u.	Upper 6/12–15	20
		Lower 2–12	14–16 (Med. epicond. 20)
Radius	8/52 i.u.	Upper 4–5	14–17
		Lower 1	18
Ulna	8/52 i.u.	Upper 9–11	14–16
		Lower 5–6	17–18
Femur	7/52 i.u.	Upper 1–12	14–17
		Lower at birth	16–18
Tibia	7/52 i.u.	Upper at birth	16–18
		Lower 10/12	15–17
Fibula	8/52 i.u.	Upper 3–4	17–19
		Lower 1	15–17

the cranial sutures by fusion (synostosis) of adjacent bones. The sequence of closure has long been regarded as giving a guide to chronological age; however, it is in fact so unreliable in modern man that it is unwise to attempt to determine the age of an unknown fossil hominid by means of correlation, even if there were grounds for suggesting that such a correlation exists.

Senile Phase. The changes of senility are degenerative; they include osteoarthritis, osteoporosis and changes in the vertebral column which produce bent posture and loss of stature. Loss of teeth is sometimes associated with senility; complete tooth loss, with resorption of alveolar bone, considerably changes the stresses acting upon the mandible, and in turn leads to bone remodelling at the gonion and the temporo-mandibular joint.

However, since all of these 'senile' changes are pathological and may occur in individuals who are not old in a chronological sense, 'senile' skeletal or dental changes must be regarded cautiously as evidence of ageing in hominid fossil material.

Teeth

Tooth morphology has played an important part in vertebrate palaeontology, if only because teeth preserve well and dental characters are   20 easily identified. The human dentition is described fully in textbooks of dental anatomy, but it may be of value to draw attention to some features of anthropological interest.

TERMINOLOGY

The hominid dental formula is the same as that of catarrhine monkeys and great apes.

Deciduous Teeth Incisors (DI) $\frac{2}{2}$ Canines (DC) $\frac{1}{1}$ Molars (DM) $\frac{2}{2}$

Permanent Teeth Incisors (I) $\frac{2}{2}$ Canines (C) $\frac{1}{1}$ Premolars (PM) $\frac{2}{2}$ Molars (M) $\frac{3}{3}$

That part of a tooth which projects above the gum is known as the crown; its surfaces are named mesial, distal, buccal, lingual and occlusal (Fig. 4).

In the case of premolars and molars, the biting or occlusal surface is modified by projections or cusps which are separated by fissures.

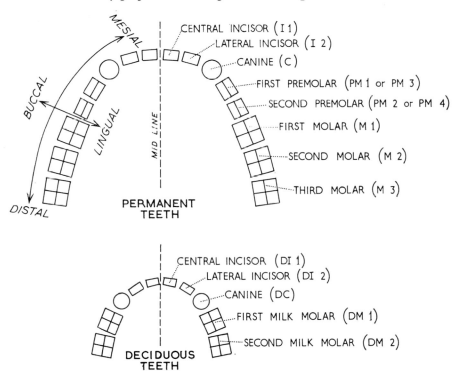

Fig. 4   The nomenclature of hominid upper and lower teeth

The general nomenclature of mammalian molar crown morphology was developed by Cope and Osborn in the late nineteenth century, and enables any cusp or ridge to be identified. The primary distinction between upper and lower molar teeth is made by adding the suffix 'id' to the name of any part of a lower molar. This allows the same terms to apply to both upper and lower molar features yet remain clearly distinguishable. The basic structure is a three-cusped triangle or *Trigon* (*Trigonid*), whose apex is lingual in upper molars and buccal in lower molars. The apical cusp is the *Protocone* (*Protoconid*), the mesial cusp the *Paracone* (*Paraconid*) and the distal cusp the *Metacone* (*Metaconid*).

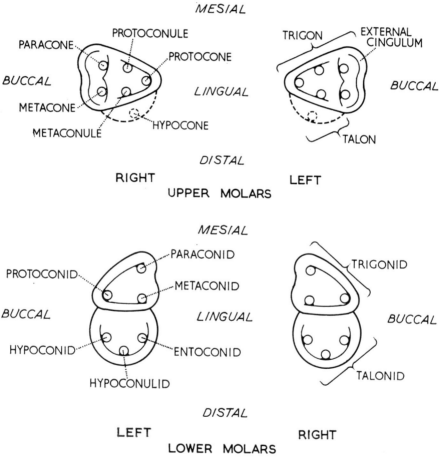

Fig. 5   The general nomenclature of mammalian molar tooth crown morphology (after Simpson, 1937)

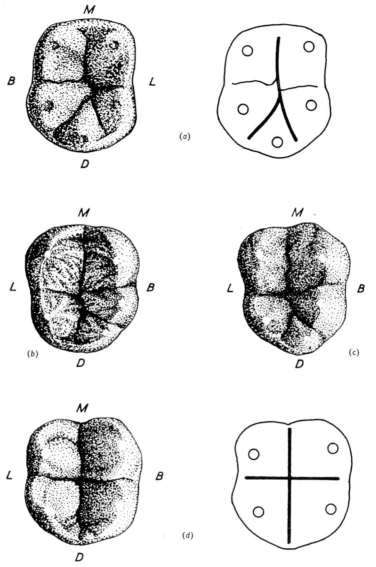

Fig. 6 The cusp and fissure pattern of pongid and hominid lower second
permanent molar teeth
(a) *Dryopithecus* (Left, Y5)   (b) Modern chimpanzee (Right, Y5)
(c) Modern man (Right, Y5)   (d) Modern man (Right, +4)

Distally the trigon (trigonid) is often extended by a basin-like *Talon* (*Talonid*) which carries a major cusp, the *Hypocone* (*Hypoconid*). The talonid frequently has a lingual *Entoconid* in addition to a hypoconid. Minor cusps which occur on ridges linking major cusps are distinguished by the suffix 'conule' (conulid), and are attributed to the nearest major cusp, for example *Protoconule* or *Hypoconulid*. A basal collar of enamel which may develop around a tooth is termed a cingulum (pl. cingula); minor cusps which arise from cingula are given the suffix 'style' (stylid) and are attributed to the related major cusp, for example *Parastyle* or *Parastylid*.

Although this terminology may appear complex it has the virtue of permitting direct reference to the features of tooth crown morphology in a wide range of mammals.

HOMINID DENTAL CHARACTERS

The principal features of hominid dentition which distinguish it from that of the great apes are the regularly curved shape of the dental arcade, reduction in the size of incisors and canines, a non-sectorial first premolar, and premolar and molar teeth with a flat occlusal wear pattern. However, the hominoid lower molar cusp pattern is basically the same as that of a Miocene ape known as *Dryopithecus*; this arrangement consists of five cusps separated by grooves in the form of a Y (Y5), and is typical of modern apes. This persisting cusp and fissure pattern is commonly found in the lower molar teeth of fossil man, but in modern man there is frequently reduction or absence of the fifth cusp (hypoconulid) and the formation of a + fissure pattern (+ 5 or + 4), particularly in the second and third molars.

TOOTH ERUPTION

The times of eruption of modern human teeth have long been known to give an indication of age. Unfortunately the ranges of normal variation are apt to be very wide so that estimations of age based on correlation within this species tend to be unreliable. It is even more hazardous to attempt to correlate the ages of tooth eruption of fossil hominids with those of modern man, other than in broad general terms.

The following table gives the approximate ages of tooth eruption for modern man.

Table 5 Approximate Ages of Tooth Eruption in Modern Man

Upper Deciduous Teeth	Months
	4 6 8 10 12 14 16 18 20 22 24 26 28 30 32 34 36
DI1	
DI2	
DC	
DM1	
DM2	

Lower Deciduous Teeth	
DI1	
DI2	
DC	
DM1	
DM2	

Upper Permanent Teeth	Years
	4 5 6 7 8 9 10 11 12 13 14 15 16 17 18 19 20 21 22 23
I1	
I2	
C	
PM1	
PM2	
M1	
M2	
M3	

Lower Permanent Teeth	
I1	
I2	
C	
PM1	
PM2	
M1	
M2	
M3	

References and Further Reading

BREATHNACH, A. S. Ed. 1958 Frazer's *Anatomy of the Human Skeleton*. 5th Ed. London: Churchill.

DAVIES, D. V. and DAVIES, F. Eds. 1964 *Gray's Anatomy: Descriptive and Applied*. 33rd Ed. London: Longmans.

ROMANES, G. J. Ed. 1964 *Cunningham's Textbook of Anatomy*. 10th Ed. Oxford: Oxford University Press.

SCOTT, J. H. and SYMONS, N. B. B. 1961 *Introduction to Dental Anatomy*. Edinburgh and London: E. and S. Livingstone.

SIMPSON, G. G. 1937 'The beginning of the age of mammals'. *Biol. Rev. 12*, 1-47.

PART III

The Fossil Hominids

The Name of the Finds

COUNTRY OF ORIGIN   REGION

Synonyms and other names The zoological names given to the specimens by other authors are quoted with the appropriate reference; in addition colloquial names in common use will be mentioned. Names given under this heading are not necessarily strict taxonomic synonyms.

Site The location of the find.

Found by The name of the field worker responsible for the find and the date.

Geology A summary of the geology and stratigraphy of the site.

Associated finds The artefacts and fossil fauna found with the remains.

Dating An assessment of the dating of the specimens.

Morphology A description of the specimens.

Dimensions Selected dimensions are given, from measurement of the original bones, from published works and, on occasion, from measurement of casts. All measurements are in millimetres unless otherwise indicated.

Affinities A summary of opinions on the nomenclature, classification and relationships of the finds.

Original The address of the institution where the remains are usually kept.

Casts Where possible the addresses are given of concerns or institutions where at one time or another casts might be obtained. No assurance can be given that casts are currently available from any of the sources mentioned.

References The principal references to the literature concerning the find.   28

Europe and the Near East

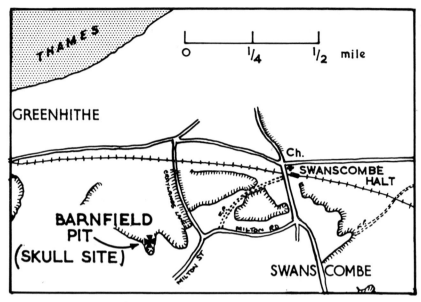

Fig. 7   The Swanscombe site

The Swanscombe Skull Fragments

Synonyms and other names

Homo cf. sapiens (Le Gros Clark *et al.*, 1938); Praesapiens man (Vallois, 1954); *Homo cf. steinheimensis* Swanscombe man

Site

Barnfield pit, half a mile south-west of All Saints Church, Swanscombe, Kent.

Found by

A. T. Marston, 29th June, 1935, and 15th March, 1936; Mr and Mrs B. O. Wymer, A. Gibson and J. Wymer, 30th July, 1955.

Geology

The bones were found in river gravel 24 feet below the surface of the 100-foot terrace of the Thames in an oblique bed at the base of the Upper Middle Gravel.

Associated finds

The implements found with the remains include numerous hand-axes and flake tools, an industry equivalent to the Middle Acheulean culture (Breuil, Acheulean III).

The fossil mammalian fauna recovered from the Swanscombe interglacial deposits includes 26 species (Sutcliffe, 1964). Amongst those recognized from the Upper Middle Gravel are wolf (*Canis cf. lupus*), lion (*Panthera spelaea*), straight tusked elephant (*Palaeoloxodon antiquus*), Merck's rhinoceros (*Didermocerus kirchbergensis = mercki*), horse (*Equus cf. caballus*), fallow deer (*Dama clactoniana*), giant deer (*Megaceros giganteus*), red deer (*Cervus elaphus*), giant ox (*Bos primigenius*) and hare (*Lepus sp.*).

Dating

On geological and faunal grounds, there seems little doubt that the deposit dates from the close of the Second Interglacial (Mindel–Riss or Penultimate Interglacial), a date which is confirmed by the type of tool culture associated with the remains.

No pollen was found in the deposits, but the fluorine content of the skull fragments and the associated mammalian bones is similar, confirming the contemporaneity of the specimens (Oakley, 1949). More recently the Second Interglacial date of the Swanscombe fragments has been reaffirmed by Kurtén (1962) and Oakley (1964).

31

Fig. 8

Fig. 9

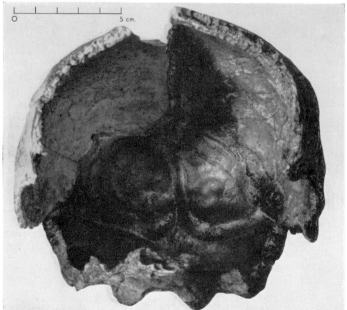

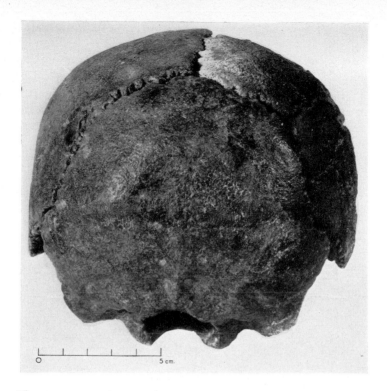

Fig. 10

Fig. 8   The Swanscombe skull
Vertical view
Courtesy of the Trustees of the British Museum (Nat. Hist.)

Fig. 9   The Swanscombe skull
Internal view
Courtesy of the Trustees of the British Museum (Nat. Hist.)

Fig. 10   The Swanscombe skull
Occipital view
Courtesy of the Trustees of the British Museum (Nat. Hist.)

Morphology The bones comprise an occipital (1935), a left parietal (1936) and a right parietal (1955). All three are almost complete and undistorted, the sutures are open and the bones clearly fit together; it is believed that they belong to a young adult female. In general the bones are of modern form, but the parietals are exceptionally thick. The occipital shows no sign of a chignon and the transverse ridge—scarcely a torus—is more prominent at its ends than in its central portion. The occipital condyles and the orientation of the foramen magnum do not differ significantly from those features in *Homo sapiens*. The sphenoidal sinus must have been large as it extends into the basi-occiput. The parietals are quadrangular and marked by the temporal lines which are well separated from each other and pass below the parietal eminence. The parietal foramina are absent and the biasterionic breadth is large. Neither parietal has a Sylvian crest on its internal surface, but the meningeal vascular pattern is complex and of unusual form by comparison with modern human bones. The grooves for the dural venous sinuses are asymmetrical.

Dimensions *Swanscombe Committee* (1938). *Morant*
Max. Length (181·5) Max. Breadth (142)
Biasterionic Breadth 123·5? Cranial Index 78?
Cranial Capacity (1,325 cc) (Mesocephalic?)

Weiner and Campbell (1964)
Biasterionic Breadth 123·0 Max. Breadth (145)

? Close approximation
( ) Estimated

Affinities The first two bones were studied by the Swanscombe Committee (Le Gros Clark *et al.*, 1938). In their report Morant showed that the metrical characters of the occipital and left parietal bones could not be distinguished from those of *Homo sapiens* with the exception of the biasterionic breadth; because of this difference and the thickness of the vault Morant suggested that the frontal bone might be like that of Steinheim man. This view has been re-expressed by Breitinger (1952 and 1955). Vallois (1954) saw no reason to suggest that Swanscombe man had brow ridges and regards Swanscombe and Fontéchevade as 'Praesapiens' forms evolving in parallel with the Steinheim–Neanderthal line. Le Gros Clark (1955) has again

34

drawn attention to the similarities between the Swanscombe and Steinheim forms, referring to both as representatives of 'Pre-Mousterian and Early Mousterian *Homo sapiens*'. Other authors are less convinced of the sapient features of Swanscombe man and emphasize the Neanderthal and primitive features of these remains (Breitinger, 1952 and 1955; Stewart, 1960). Howell (1960) affirmed that the known fragments from Swanscombe and Steinheim indicate that both forms represent the same hominid variety and that they 'deviate from the anatomically modern morphological pattern and, instead, are allied with early Neanderthal peoples'.

The Swanscombe site and fossil material have been thoroughly reinvestigated recently (Brothwell *et al.*, 1964). Following a morphological, metrical and statistical reappraisal of the skull bones, Weiner and Campbell (1964) emphasized the degree of interrelatedness between the forms of *Homo*, i.e. Solo, Rhodesian, Neanderthal and modern man. They suggest that it is not possible to maintain, in a taxonomic sense, strictly specific status for each of these forms, regarding them as a 'spectrum' of varieties within one species. Swanscombe man has been regarded as belonging to the Neanderthaloid 'intermediate' group which contains the Steinheim, Ehringsdorf, Skūhl V and Krapina specimens.

Originals British Museum (Natural History), Cromwell Road,
South Kensington, London, S.W.7.

Casts The University Museum, University of Pennsylvania,
Philadelphia 4, Pennsylvania, U.S.A.

References MARSTON, A. T. 1936
Preliminary note on a new fossil human skull from Swanscombe, Kent. *Nature 138*, 200-201.
MARSTON, A. T. 1937
The Swanscombe skull. *J. R. anthrop. Inst. 67*, 339-406.
CLARK, W. E. LE GROS, OAKLEY, K. P., MORANT, G. M., KING, W. B. R., HAWKES, C. F. C., *et. al.* 1938
Report of the Swanscombe Committee. *J. R. anthrop. Inst. 68*, 17-98.
OAKLEY, K. P., and MONTAGU, M. F. A. 1949
A reconsideration of the Galley Hill skeleton. *Bull. Brit. Mus. (Nat. Hist.) 1*, 27-46.
BREITINGER, E. 1952
Zur Morphologie und systematischer Stellung des Schädelfragmentes von Swanscombe. *Homo 3*, 131-133.

OAKLEY, K. P. 1952
Swanscombe man. *Proc. Geol. Ass. Lond. 63*, 271-300.

VALLOIS, H. V. 1954
Neandertals and praesapiens. *J. R. anthrop. Inst. 84*, 111-130

BREITINGER, E. *1955*
Das Schädelfragmentes von Swanscombe und das 'Praesapiens-problem'. *Mitt. anthrop. Ges. Wien 84/85*, 1-45.

CLARK, W. E. LE GROS 1955
The fossil evidence for human evolution. Chicago: Chicago University Press.

WYMER, J. 1955
A further fragment of the Swanscombe skull. *Nature 176*, 426-427

OAKLEY, K. P. 1957
Stratigraphical age of the Swanscombe skull. *Am. J. Phys. Anthrop. 15*, 253-260.

STEWART, T. D. 1960
Indirect evidence of the primitiveness of the Swanscombe skull. *Am. J. Phys. Anthrop. 18*, 363.

HOWELL, F. C. 1960
European and northwest African Middle Pleistocene hominids. *Curr. Anthrop. 1*, 195-232

KURTÉN, B. 1962
The relative ages of the australopithecines of Transvaal and the pithecanthropines of Java. *In Evolution und Hominisation.* Ed. G. Kurth, pp. 74-80. Stuttgart: Gustav Fischer Verlag.

BROTHWELL, D. R., CAMPBELL, B. G., CASTELL, C. P., GARDINER, E., OAKLEY, K. P., PATTERSON, C., SUTCLIFFE, A. J., SWINTON, W. E., WEINER, J. S., WYMER, J. 1964.
In *The Swanscombe Skull.* Ed. C. D. Ovey. Royal Anthropological Institute, *Occasional Paper No. 20.* London: Royal Anthropological institute.

The La Chapelle-aux-Saints Skeleton

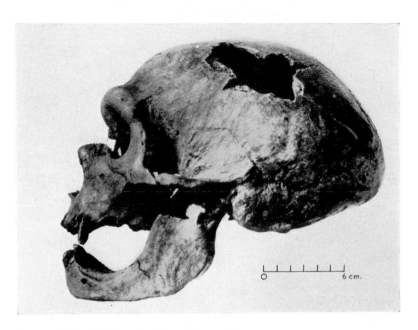

Fig. 11   The skull from La Chapelle-aux-Saints
Courtesy of the Director of the Musée de l'Homme

Synonyms   Homo neanderthalensis (Boule, 1911–1913); *Homo   sapiens*
and other names   *neanderthalensis* (Campbell, 1964)
Neanderthal man, Neandertal man

Site   Near the village of La Chapelle-aux-Saints, 25 miles south-
east of Brive, Corrèze, France.

Found by   A. and J. Bouyssonie and L. Bardon, 3rd August, 1908.

Geology   The skeleton was found buried in the floor of a small cave
hollowed into the limestone of the Lower Lias, which rests
upon Triassic sandstone. The skeleton was covered with
calcareous clay containing stones which had fallen from the
roof. The stratigraphy was carefully recorded whilst the
remains were uncovered.

Associated finds   With the bones were numerous flint tools of an evolved
Mousterian culture including retouched blades, scrapers and   37

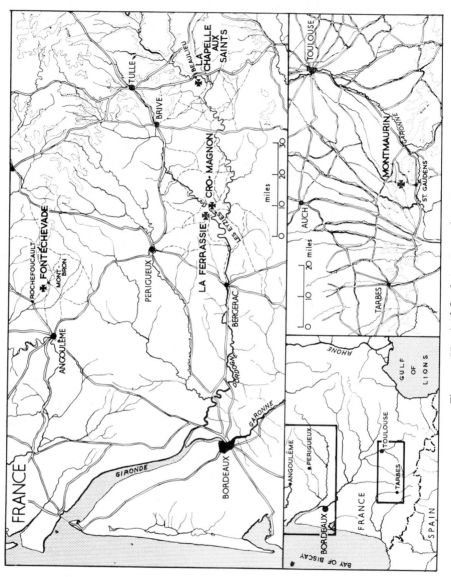

Fig. 12 Hominid fossil sites in southern France

keeled scrapers which are almost Aurignacian. In addition there were numerous fossil bones which belonged to mammals such as woolly rhinoceros (*Coelodonta antiquitatis*), reindeer (*Rangifer tarandus*), ibex (*Capra ibex*), hyena (*Crocuta crocuta*), marmot (*Arctomys marmotta*), wild horse (*Equus sp.*), bison (*Bison priscus*) and wolf (*Canis lupus*).

Dating In view of the 'cold weather' fauna and the tool culture the skeleton has been attributed to the Upper Pleistocene, probably the Fourth Glacial period (Würm or Last Glaciation).

Morphology The skeleton is almost complete and belonged to an adult male. It comprises the skull, twenty-one vertebrae, twenty ribs, one clavicle, two humeri, two radii, two ulnae, several hand bones including one scaphoid, one capitate, metacarpals I, II, III and V, as well as two proximal phalanges. The lower limbs are represented by two pelvic fragments, two femora, two patellae, parts of two tibiae, one fibula, one calcaneum, one talus, five metatarsals and several other fragmentary bones. The bones have been described by Boule (1911–1913) in detail, and the skeleton has been designated the type specimen of the species *Homo neanderthalensis*.

THE SKULL

The skull is large and well preserved, having a low vault and a receding forehead. The supra-orbital arches are large but the mastoid processes are small. The occipital bone protrudes into a characteristic bun-shape. The orbits are voluminous, the nose broad and the mandible stout but chinless. The bony palate is very large, but all the teeth are missing except for the upper and lower second left premolars.

THE POST-CRANIAL BONES

In general the limb bones are short and thick, with strong markings and large joints. The humeri are straight but the femora are bowed; similarly the radii are curved, having a medial concavity. The tibiae are short and stout, and their upper ends appear to be bent backwards into a position of retroversion. The fibula is robust. The hand and foot bones are not unlike those of modern man; the scaphoid and capitate seem small, but the metacarpals are stout with large heads. The foot bones are rugged, the talus in particular being high   39 and short-necked; the calcaneum is robust and has a prominent sustentacular shelf.

The vertebral column, as described by Boule (1911–1913), is said to have long, backwardly directed cervical spinous processes which are frequently bifid. The cervical and lumbar curvatures of the spine are obliterated and the remainder of the vertebrae are said to be short-bodied.

In view of the features of the post-cranial skeleton, Boule suggested that the stance of La Chapelle man (Neanderthal man) was stooping with flexed hips and knees and jutting head carriage, and his undoubtedly bipedal gait imperfect and slouching. Recent re-examination of the skeleton (Arambourg, 1955; Cave and Straus, 1957; Patte, 1955) has shown that there is evidence of gross deforming osteoarthritis present in the specimen and that Boule's reconstruction is faulty in a number of respects. In addition, comparison with other Neanderthal remains and a wider range of modern skeletal material has shown that many of the features recognized as being characteristically Neanderthal fall within the range of modern human skeletal variation. Whilst Cave and Straus (1957) do not deny the distinctive morphological characters of Neanderthal man, they suggest that he stood and walked as does modern man.

Dimensions   *Boule (1911–1913), Patte (1955)*
SKULL
Max. Length 208   Max. Breadth 156
Cranial Capacity 1,620 cc   Cranial Index 75·0
(Dolichocephalic)
Symphysial Angle of Mandible 104°
POST–CRANIAL BONES

	Length	Circumference		Torsion
Right humerus	313		72	148°
Left humerus	—		65	—
Radius Length	235★	A/P diam.	12·0	Width 16·0
Ulna Length	255–260★	Upper Arm/Forearm		
		Carrying Angle 179°		
Capite Length	24·0	Breadth	14·0	

★ Restored.

40

	I	II	Metacarpals III	IV	V
Length	44·5	73·0*	71·0*	—	54·0
Min. diam.	11·0	7·5	8·0	—	6·5

Femur Length 430* (R)   A/P diam. 31·0 (L)   Trans.
                                                 diam. 29·0 (L)

Tibiae   —   Damaged   —
Talus Length/Breadth Index 107·5   Horiz. Angle of
                                          Neck 23°

Calcaneum Length 80*   Breadth 47
* Restored.

Numerous measurements and indices relating to the La Chapelle skeleton are quoted by Patte (1955).

Affinities The similarities between the skeleton from Neanderthal and that from La Chapelle-aux-Saints leave little doubt that they belong to the same species. Further finds have established that these men were widely distributed in Europe and the Near East during the Upper Pleistocene period. Their sudden disappearance and replacement by modern forms of man remains a topic for speculation and investigation. It is uncertain whether they became extinct because of the invasion of more advanced hominids, or became assimilated by the evolving population of modern man, or directly gave rise to modern man, an older view revived by Brace (1964). In a recent classification of the *Hominidae*, Campbell (1964) has identified Neanderthal man as a subspecies of *Homo sapiens* (*Homo sapiens neanderthalensis*).

Original Musée de l'Homme, Palais de Chaillot, Paris–16ᵉ, France.

Casts 1 Musée de l'Homme, Paris (Cranium and endocranium).
2 The University Museum, University of Pennsylvania, Philadelphia 4, Pennsylvania, U.S.A. (Restored skull only).

References BOULE, M. 1908
L'Homme fossile de la Chapelle-aux-Saints (Corrèze). *C. R. Acad. Sci. Paris. 147*, 1349–1352.
BOULE, M. 1908
L'Homme fossile de La Chapelle-aux-Saints. *Anthropologie 19*, 519–525.

BOUYSSONIE, A. and J., and BARDON, L. 1908
Découverte d'un squelette humain moustérien à La Chapelle-aux-Saints, Corrèze. *C. R. Acad. Sci. Paris 147*, 1414-1415.

BOULE, M. 1911-1913
L'Homme fossile de La Chapelle-aux-Saints. *Annls de Paléont. 6, 7, and 8.*

HRDLIČKA, A. 1930
The skeletal remains of early man. *Smithson. misc. Coll. 83*, 1-379.

ARAMBOURG, C. 1955
Sur l'attitude, en station verticale, des Néanderthaliens. *C. R. Acad. Sci. Paris 240*, 804-806.

PATTE, E. 1955
Les Néanderthaliens: Anatomie, Physiologie, Comparaisons. Paris; Masson et Cie.

CAVE, A. J. E., and STRAUS, W. L., Jnr. 1957
Pathology and posture of Neanderthal man. *Quart. Rev. Biol. 32*, 348-363.

BRACE, C. L. 1964
A consideration of hominid catastrophism. *Curr. Anthrop. 5*, 3-43.

CAMPBELL, B. 1964
Quantitative taxonomy and human evolution. In *Classification and human evolution.* Ed. S. L. Washburn. pp. 50-74. London: Methuen and Co. Ltd.

The La Ferrassie Skeletons

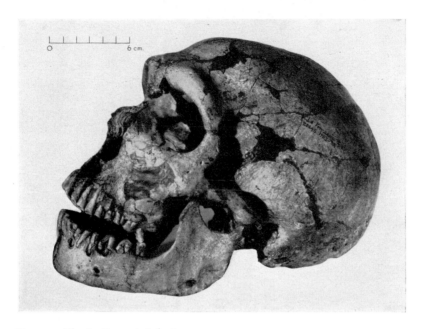

Fig. 13   The La Ferrassie I skull
Courtesy of the Director of the Musée de l'Homme

Synonyms and other names	*Homo neanderthalensis* (Boule, 1911–1913); *Homo sapiens neanderthalensis* (Campbell, 1964) Neanderthal man; Neandertal man
Site	La Ferrassie, north of Bugue, Dordogne, France.
Found by	R. Capitan and D. Peyrony, 17th September, 1909 (No. 1), 1910 (No. 2), 8th August, 1912 (Nos. 3 and 4), and in 1920 and 1921 (Nos. 5 and 6).
Geology	The remains were in a rock shelter. The stratigraphy, determined by a group of eminent French prehistorians, was said to be the same as that found at La Chapelle-aux-Saints. The skeletons were found below three Aurignacian levels at the bottom of a layer containing Mousterian tools; this in turn rested upon another layer containing Acheulean implements. The

43

bones of the first skeleton were lying in anatomical relation with each other and the layers were undisturbed.

Associated finds The tools found with the skeletons are of the Mousterian culture. The first mammalian bones recovered from the same deposit include those of mammoth (*Mammuthus primigenius*), hyena (*Crocuta crocuta*), pig (*Sus sp.*), ox (*Bos sp.*), red deer (*Cervus elaphus*) and horse (*Equus sp.*).

Dating The tools and fauna suggest an Upper Pleistocene date for the remains, probably during the Fourth Glacial period (Würm or Last Glaciation).

Morphology Skeleton No. 1 is that of an adult male and skeleton No. 2 an adult female; both are virtually complete. Nos. 3 and 4 are those of infants and Nos. 5 and 6 those of an infant and a foetus. All of the immature skeletons are fragmentary.

Unfortunately none of the material has been fully studied. Only a partial description is available (Boule, 1911–1913), nevertheless it is clear that the skeletons have much in common with previously known Neanderthal remains.

THE SKULL

The male skull (No. 1) has stout supra-orbital ridges, a flattened vault with recession of the forehead, a protuberant occiput and small mastoid processes. The hard palate is broad and limited by an almost parabolic dental arcade. The mandible is perhaps more modern than that of La Chapelle man. It has a feeble chin, a deep mandibular notch and large coronoid processes. The teeth are all in place in both jaws, with no diastema. All of the teeth are badly worn so that no details of crown morphology are discernible.

In occlusion there is slight anterior displacement of the mandible so that the lower incisors project slightly in front of the upper incisors (negative overjet).

THE POST-CRANIAL BONES

The limb bones resemble those of La Chapelle man in their principal features, tending to be robust with large joints. The tibiae have retroverted heads and the fibulae are stout.

It is fortunate that the adult skeletons have well preserved feet and hands because their study should reveal a great deal about the way in which Neanderthal man stood and walked, as well as indicating the types of grip which his hand structure per- 44

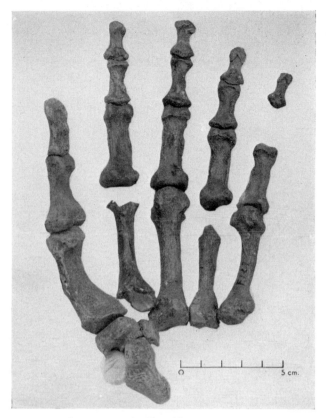

Fig. 14   The La Ferrassie I hand bones
An articulation of casts

mitted. No detailed studies of this sort have been published as
yet, but examination of the original foot bones (No. 1) shows
that the great toe is not divergent, the longitudinal and
transverse arches of the foot are well formed and that the
general foot structure corresponds with that of modern man.
These characteristics suggest that the stance and gait of La
Ferrassie man differed little from that of *Homo sapiens*. The
hand bones are stout, the carpal arch is deep and the carpo-
metacarpal joint of the thumb is saddle-shaped; these features
should permit the thumb to rotate into a position from which
good opposability is possible and perhaps would allow of both
a power and a precision grip.

45

Dimensions   Boule (1911–1913), *Vallois* (1954)
SKULL (La Ferrassie I)
Max. Length 209   Max. Breadth 158
Cranial Capacity 1,641 cc.   Cranial Index 75·5
(Dolichocephalic)
Symphysial Angle of Mandible 85°

POST-CRANIAL BONES

	L.F. I	L.F. II
Upper arm/Forearm Carrying Angle	177°	179°
Tibiae Right Max. Length 308		
Left Max. Length 307		

Capitan and Peyrony (1921)
Infant Femur Length 150

Affinities   The features of the skeletons indicate that they belong to the group of Neanderthal men represented by the original Neanderthal skeleton and the skeleton from La Chapelle-aux-Saints. This group is characterized by numerous skeletal similarities as well as by their general contemporaneity, and had led to their designation as 'classic' Neanderthalers of the Würm glaciation. In a recent classification, Campbell (1964), Neanderthal man is identified as a subspecies of *Homo sapiens* (*Homo sapiens neanderthalensis*).

Originals   *Skeletons Nos. 1 to 4*—Musée de l'Homme, Palais de Chaillot, Paris–16ᵉ, France.
Skeletons Nos. 5 and 6—Musée des Eyzies, Les Eyzies, Dordogne, France.

Casts   Not available at present.

References   CAPITAN, L. and PEYRONY, D. 1909
Deux squelettes humains au milieu de foyers de l'époque moustérienne. *Rev. anthrop. 19*, 402-409.
CAPITAN, L. and PEYRONY, D. 1911
Un nouveau squelette humain fossile. *Rev. anthrop. 21*, 148-150.
BOULE, M. 1911-1913
L'Homme fossile de La Chapelle-aux-Saints. *Annls de Paléont. 6, 7* and 8.
CAPITAN, L. and PEYRONY, D. 1912
Station préhistorique de la Ferrassie. *Rev. anthrop. 22*, 76-99.
CAPITAN, L. and PEYRONY, D. 1912
Trois nouveaux squelettes humains fossiles. *Rev. anthrop. 22*, 439-442.

CAPITAN, L. and PEYRONY, D. 1921
Nouvelles fouilles à la Ferrassie, Dordogne. *C. R. Ass. franç. Av. Sci. 44ᵉ Session*, 540-542.

CAPITAN, L. and PEYRONY, D. 1921
Découverte d'un sixième squelette moustérien à la Ferrassie, Dordogne. *Rev. anthrop. 31*, 382-388.

HRDLIČKA, A. 1930
The skeletal remains of early man. *Smithson. misc. Coll. 83*, 1-379.

PATTE, E. 1955
Les Néanderthaliens: Anatomie, Physiologie, Comparaisons. Paris: Masson et Cie.

CAMPBELL, B. 1964
Quantitative taxonomy and human evolution. In *Classification and human evolution*. Ed. S. L. Washburn. pp. 50-74. London: Methuen and Co. Ltd.

The Cro-Magnon Remains

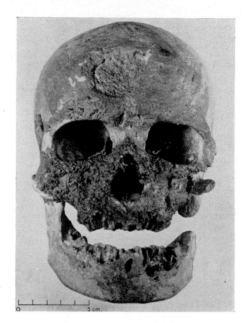

Fig. 15 The 'Old man' from Cro-
Magnon.
*Courtesy of the Director of
the Musée de l'Homme*

Synonyms and other names	*Homo sapiens sapiens* Cro-magnon man
Site	Cro-Magnon, near Les Eyzies, Dordogne, France.
Found by	L. Lartet, 1868.
Geology	During the construction of a railway along the Vézère valley, excavation of a Cretaceous limestone cliff uncovered a rock shelter which had become filled by rock falls and debris. At the back of the shelter, under well recognizable occupation floors, were the remains of five adult skeletons and some fragmentary infant and foetal bones. It appeared that the bones had been deliberately buried.
Associated finds	With the skeletons were numerous flint tools of Aurignacian manufacture, and large numbers of sea shells, some of which were pierced. The fossil bones of mammals recovered from the site included reindeer (*Rangifer tarandus*), bison (*Bison priscus*), mammoth (*Mammuthus primigenius*) and horse (*Equus sp.*).
Dating	The bones, unearthed by L. Lartet, an experienced geologist,

48

were stratigraphically contemporaneous with the deposit; the fauna and the tool culture suggested an Upper Pleistocene date for the burials, probably during the Fourth Glaciation (Würm or Last Glaciation).

Morphology The best-preserved skull belonged to an adult male known colloquially as the 'Old Man' of Cro-Magnon, although he was possibly a little under 50 years of age at his death (Vallois, 1937). It was upon the description of this skeleton that the principal features of the 'Cro-Magnon race' were based.

SKULL

The skull is virtually complete and undamaged except for missing mandibular condyles and a lack of teeth. The cranium is large and long with the vault somewhat flattened, and the outline of the skull from above is five-sided—the 'dolicho-pentagonal' form of some authors. In profile the forehead is steep and the superciliary ridges weak, the parieto-occipital region is curiously flattened in the midline and the parietal bosses are prominent. The face is broad and short with compressed rectangular orbits, whilst the tall narrow nasal opening and constricted nasal root make the nasal bones project. The subnasal maxilla slopes forward producing a moderate degree of alveolar prognathism. The bony palate is elevated centrally and grooved strongly for the palatal vessels and nerves. The dental arcade, as judged by the alveolar process of bone, is parabolic.

POST-CRANIAL BONES

The limb bones suggest that this individual was tall and muscular since the bones are long and the impressions for muscle and ligamentous attachments are strongly developed. The tibia is described as flattened and sabre-like (platycnemia), and the fibula deeply grooved.

Dimensions SKULL

Broca (1868)
Max. Length 202   Max. Breadth 149
Cranial capacity 1,590 cc   Cranial Index 73·8
(Dolichocephalic)

Morant, G. (1930–1931)
Max. Length 202·5   Max. Breadth 149·5
Cranial Index 73·8
(Dolichocephalic)

49

POST-CRANIAL BONES

Femur—Length 394   (Epiphysis missing)

Tibia—Length 323   (Epiphysis missing)

Affinities   There is no doubt that the general skeletal morphology of this Cro-Magnon man shows that he belongs to *Homo sapiens*, but several features of the bones when taken as a group serve to distinguish this skeleton from those representing modern man. This group of characteristics has been used to define the 'Cro-Magnon race' of the Upper Pleistocene. Skeletal remains having these general features have been collected from many parts of western Europe, including France (Abri-Pataud, Dordogne; Bruniquel; Chancelade; Combe-Capelle; Gourdan; Les Hoteaux dans l'Ain; La Madelaine; Mentone and Solutré), Germany (Obercassel; Stettin), Great Britain (Paviland, Glamorgan), Italy (Grimaldi), Czechoslovakia (Brno and Predmost, Moravia) and many other sites.

The remains from the Grottes des Enfants, Grimaldi, include two skeletons whose features have been regarded as negroid and thus may represent a distinct Upper Palaeolithic race; similarly the Chancelade remains have been likened to the skeletons of modern Eskimos and distinguished as the 'Chancelade race'.

Whether or not these are valid distinctions it is apparent that European Upper Palaeolithic men exhibited a wide range of variation in skeletal form. Moreover, it is clear that they used stone and bone in a variety of ways, producing implements, ornamental objects and cave paintings. The tools made by these peoples have been classified in many ways but three main groups predominate: the Aurignacian, Magdalenian and Solutrean cultures.

The origin of the Cro-Magnon people is still in some doubt because of the paucity of the fossil remains of their probable ancestors (for example Swanscombe and Fontéchevade); similarly their relationship with the Neanderthalers—at least some of whom were contemporaneous with Upper Pleistocene *Homo sapiens*—is an open question. It has been held variously that *Homo sapiens* displaced the Neanderthalers who became extinct or that the spreading *Homo sapiens* population absorbed the Neanderthalers. Most recently an older view has been revived suggesting that *Homo sapiens* arose directly from a Neanderthal stock (Brace, 1964).

The Cro-Magnon Remains

Originals   Musée de l'Homme, Palais de Chaillot, Paris–16ᵉ, France.

Casts   1   Musée de l'Homme, Palais de Chaillot, Paris–16ᵉ, France.
(Skull 1 and mandible, Skull 2 and Skull 3, one femur, two tibiae, one humerus, one ulna, one fibula).

2   The University Museum, University of Pennsylvania, Philadelphia 4, Pennsylvania, U.S.A.
(Skull 1 reconstruction).

References   BROCA, P. 1865-1875
On the human skulls and bones found in the cave of Cro-Magnon, near Les Eyzies. In *Reliquiae aquitanicae*. E. Lartet and H. Christy. Ed. T. R. Jones. London: Williams and Norgate, pp. 97-122.
BROCA, P. 1868
Sur les crânes et les ossements des Eyzies. *Bull. Soc. Anthrop. Paris 3*, 350-392.
QUATREFAGES, A. DE, and HAMY, E. 1882
Races humaines fossiles. In *Crania Ethnica*, pp. 44-54 and 81-82. Paris: J. B. Baillière et Fils.
MORANT, G. 1930-1931
Studies of Palaeolithic man, IV. *Ann. Eugen., Lond. 4*, 109-214.
BONIN, G. VON 1935
European races of the Upper Palaeolithic. *Hum. Biol. 7*, 196-221.
VALLOIS, H. V. 1937
La durée de la vie chez l'homme fossile. *Anthropologie 47, 499-532,*

The Fontéchevade Skull Bones

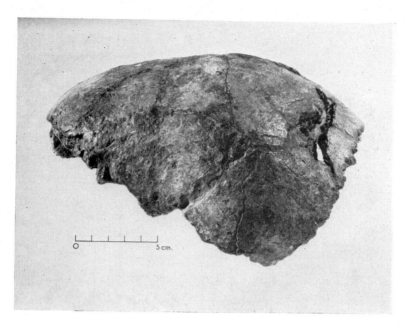

Fig. 16   The Fontéchevade II skull bones
Courtesy of the Director of the Musée de l'Homme

Synonyms and other names	Homo 'praesapiens' Praesapiens man (Vallois, 1949c) Fontéchevade man
Site	Fontéchevade, near Montbron, Charente, about 17 miles east of Angoulême, France.
Found by	Mlle. G. Henri-Martin, 16th August, 1947.
Geology	The Fontéchevade cave is cut into the wall of the valley of the river Tardoire. During the excavation of the cave floor, which had been previously investigated, a thick layer of stalagmite was exposed. Beneath this layer were found deposits which contained a fossil hominid calotte and part of a frontal bone. The layer of stalagmite has separated the cave filling into two principal strata and indicates a considerable time difference between them.

52

The Fontéchevade Skull Bones

Associated finds The original excavation had removed material containing Magdalenian, Aurignacian and Mousterian implements, but no hominid remains. The layer beneath the stalagmite contained primitive Tayacian flake tools in its upper part, whilst lower in this stratum the tools were Clactonian, an industry which is even more primitive in its workmanship.

The fossil fauna associated with the hominid remains includes rhinoceros (*Didermocerus sp.*), fallow deer (*Dama sp.*), tortoise (*Testudo graeca*) and bear (*Ursus sp.*): a warm/temperate interglacial fauna.

Dating The fossil layer has been attributed to the Third Interglacial period (Riss–Würm or Last Interglacial) in view of the fauna and the tool culture which it contains. The contemporaneity of the hominid fossils with the associated fauna has been established by means of the fluorine test (Oakley and Hoskins, 1951).

Morphology FONTÉCHEVADE II

The principal specimen consists of both parietals and part of the frontal bone. They are joined together and most of the sutures are obliterated. The right parietal is complete but the anterior portion of the frontal and the inferior border of the left parietal are missing. According to Vallois (1949b) the bones have been affected by fire. The external surfaces of the parietals are relatively featureless, having no parietal foramina, temporal lines or parietal bosses. The vault is somewhat flattened but the forehead is steep with no evidence of post-orbital constriction or supra-orbital torus. Viewed from above the skull is pentagonal, its greatest breadth being in the parietal region. The bones of the vault are absolutely and relatively thick.

FONTÉCHEVADE I

The smaller fragment is part of a frontal bone. It resembles the previous specimen in that it shows no evidence of a supra-orbital torus but its vault is thinner.

Dimensions Vallois (1958)   FONTÉCHEVADE II
Max. Breadth (154)   Length (195)
Cranial Index 78·9*   Cranial Capacity Approx. 1,470 cc
Biasterionic breadth (126)
( ) Specimen damaged
* Calculated figure

53

Affinities The general features of the Fontéchevade calotte resemble those of *Homo sapiens* (Vallois, 1949b), in particular the shape of the forehead and the form of the parietal bones; on the other hand it is distinguished by the flattening of the vault, the thickness of the bones and the large biasterionic breadth. In these latter features it can be likened to the Swanscombe skull or to the Neanderthalers. The lack of a developed frontal torus is considered by Vallois to rule out a close relationship with the Neanderthalers or with pre-Neanderthal forms. He states, therefore, that it is established that European *Homo sapiens* is not derived from the Neanderthal men who preceded him (Vallois, 1954). It was because of the similarities between Swanscombe man and Fontéchevade man that they have been grouped as 'Praesapiens' hominids until more is known of the characters of the face and jaw of either or both forms (Vallois, 1949b, 1954 and 1958). The term 'Praesapiens' is alleged to be morphologically valid, but the extent to which it indicates evolutionary continuity is not yet known. Vallois's interpretation of the Fontéchevade remains has been questioned by Howell (1957), the evidence being regarded as 'not fully conclusive'. Later, in a controversial article which has been severely criticized, Brace (1964) casts doubt upon the dating, reconstruction and interpretation of the Fontéchevade material which he does not accept as representative of early or pre-Neanderthal *Homo sapiens*. It is apparent that the relationships of Fontéchevade man are still in dispute and are likely to remain so until more evidence is available.

Originals Musée de l'Homme, Palais de Chaillot, Paris–16e, France.

Casts Not generally available at present.

References
HENRI-MARTIN, G. 1947
L'Homme fossile tayacien de la grotte de Fontéchevade. *C. R. Acad. Sci. Paris 225*, 766–767
VALLOIS, H. V. 1949a.
L'Homme fossile de Fontéchevade *C. R. Acad. Sci. Paris 228*, 598–600
VALLOIS, H. V. 1949b
The Fontéchevade fossil man. *Am. J. Phys. Anthrop. 7*, 339–362.
VALLOIS, H. V. 1949c
L'origine de l'*Homo sapiens*. *C. R. Acad. Sci. Paris 228*, 949–951.
OAKLEY, K. P. and HOSKINS, C. R. 1951
Application du 'Test de la Fluorine' aux crânes de Fontéchevade. *Anthropologie 55*, 239–242.

HENRI-MARTIN, G. 1951
Rémarques sur la stratigraphie de la grotte de Fontéchevade (Charente). *Anthropologie* 55, 242-247.

VALLOIS, H. V. 1954
Neandertals and Praesapiens. *J. R. anthrop. Inst. 84*, 111-130.

HOWELL, F. C. 1957
The evolutionary significance of variation and varieties of 'Neanderthal man'. *Quart. Rev. Biol. 32*, 330-347.

VALLOIS, H. V. 1958
La grotte de Fontéchevade II. *Archs Inst. Paléont. hum. 29*, 1-262.

BRACE, C. L. 1964
A consideration of hominid catastrophism. *Curr. Anthrop. 5*, 3-43.

The Montmaurin Remains

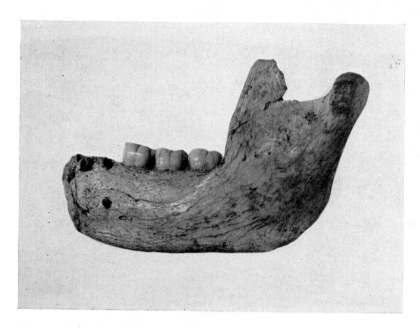

Fig. 17   The Montmaurin mandible
Courtesy of the Director of the Musée de l'Homme

Synonyms and other names	*Homo* aff. *neanderthalensis* Montmaurin man
Site	The 'Coupe Gorge' cave, which is hollowed into the lime-stone cliff forming the valley of the Seygouade, Montmaurin, eight miles north of Saint-Gaudens, Haute-Garonne, France.
Found by	An amateur prehistorian, M. R. Cammas, and his colleagues, 18th July, 1949.
Geology	The remains were found during excavation of the cave floor and an infilled vertical shaft (La Niche) which had probably communicated with the main cave in the past but has gradually become filled. The cave-filling showed evidence of stratification but the shaft-filling did not.
Associated finds	The artefacts recovered from the lower levels of the cave are principally made of quartzite but some are of flint. The work-

56

manship of the tools shows that they belong to a pre–Mousterian culture.

Bed 3 of the cave-filling contains fossil mammalian bones which indicate a warm climate, and include horse (*Equus sp.*), bear (*Ursus sp.*) and red deer (*Cervus elaphus*). The shaft also contains the fossil bones of mammals similar to those found in Bed 3 of the cave, but the preponderant form in this deposit is the red deer (*Cervus elaphus*). In neither deposit were there remains of reindeer, which again suggests that the climate was warm when the bones were buried. Although this is agreed by most authors, opinion has been divided as to which interglacial (or interstadial) period the deposit should be referred.

Dating   By means of a geological method Bonifay (1956) showed two cold maxima in the cave-filling, Bed 3 and Bed 7, which he attributed to the beginning of the Würm and the end of the Riss Glaciations respectively. The remains found in the cave were in Bed 3, but the principal find was uncovered much lower in the shaft-filling although the fauna of the shaft is similar to that of Bed 3. Vallois (1956) was undecided and suggested either a Riss–Würm or a Mindel–Riss Interglacial date for these remains, but Kurtén (1962) placed them in the Second Interglacial (Mindel–Riss or Penultimate Interglacial) with Swanscombe and Steinheim man (*q.v.*).

Morphology   *Vallois (1956), Howell (1960)*
Four teeth were recovered from Bed 3 of the cave deposit, an incisor, a canine, a premolar and a molar; the shaft yielded an almost complete mandible and a vertebra. Only the mandible has been described as yet.

THE MANDIBLE
The mandible is relatively small by comparison with other specimens both fossil and recent, but it is stoutly constructed. All six molar teeth are in place. The body is thick with parallel borders and double mental foramina, and posteriorly the inferior border has a prominent tubercle. The symphysial region is sharply receding and there is no chin. The inner aspect of the symphysis has a torus, below which there is a hollow bearing a median eminence in the position of the genial tubercles. The digastric impressions are extensive,   57

reaching back as far as the first molar teeth, but there are no sublingual fossae. The rami are of moderate breadth, bearing large coronoid and condyloid processes separated by well marked mandibular notches. The angles of the mandible are rounded and the bicondylar breadth is large. The dental arcade is parabolic and divergent.

TEETH

The molar teeth decrease in size in the order M3 > M1 > M2 and the crown cusp pattern is dryopithecine; sixth cusps and hypoconulids are present but no cingula. The third molars show signs of secondary enamel wrinkling and the pulp cavities are moderately taurodont.

Dimensions *Vallois* (1956)
Symphysial Angle 101°
Symphysial Angle (to the alveolar plane) 73° (Vallois and Roche, 1958)
Ramus Breadth Index 64·7

Affinities According to Vallois (1956), the Montmaurin jaw is typically Neanderthal in its principal features but it has a few character- istics which recall the Mauer mandible (*q.v.*). In an earlier paper (1955) it was suggested that the Montmaurin mandible 'fits' the Steinheim cranium. It is clear therefore that Vallois sees this mandible as a representative of a pre-Neanderthal stage, morphologically intermediate between Mauer man and the Neanderthalers. More recently Howell (1960) also tenta- tively suggested that the Mauer mandible was merely an early representative of the same Montmaurin–Neanderthal lineage. Until the mandibles of the Steinheim–Swanscombe peoples or the cranium of the Mauer people are known the relationships of these Middle Pleistocene hominids must remain obscure.

Original Musée de l'Homme, Palais de Chaillot, Paris–16ᵉ, France.

Casts Not generally available at present.

References BAYLAC, P., CAMMAS, R., *et al.* 1950
Découverte récentes dans les grottes de Montmaurin, Haute-Garonne. *Anthropologie 54*, 262-271.
VALLOIS, H. V. 1955
La mandibule humaine pré-moustérienne de Montmaurin. *C. R. Acad. Sci. Paris 240*, 1577-1579.

58

BONIFAY, E. 1956
Les sédiments détritiques grossiers dans les remplissages des grottes. Méthode d'étude morphologique et statistique. *Anthropologie 60*, 447-461.

VALLOIS, H. V. 1956
The pre-Mousterian mandible from Montmaurin. *Am. J. Phys. Anthrop. 14*, 319-323.

VALLOIS, H. V. and ROCHE, J. 1958
La mandibule Acheuléene de Témara Maroc. *C. R. Acad. Sci. Paris 246*, 3113-3116.

HOWELL, F. C. 1960
European and northwest African Middle Pleistocene hominids. *Curr. Anthrop. 1*, 195-232.

KURTÉN, B. 1962
The relative ages of the australopithecines of Transvaal and the pithecanthropines of Java. In *Evolution und Hominisation*. Ed. G. Kurth, pp. 74-80. Stuttgart: Gustav Fischer Verlag.

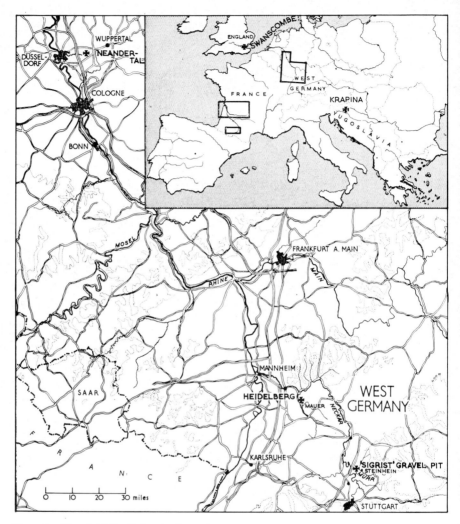

Fig. 18   Hominid fossil sites in Central Europe

The Neanderthal Skeleton

Synonyms
and other names

Homo neanderthalensis (King, 1864); Homo sapiens neanderthalensis (Campbell, 1964)
Neanderthal man; Neandertal man
Numerous other names have been proposed for Neanderthal forms, amongst them Homo primigenius, Homo antiquus, Homo incipiens, Homo europaeus, Homo mousteriensis. None of them precedes the name given by King and none is in common use.

Site
The Neandertal valley, near Hochdal, about seven miles east of Dusseldorf, towards Wuppertal.

Found by
Workmen; recognized by von Fuhlrott, August, 1856.

Geology
The skeleton was uncovered when a cave deposit was disturbed during quarrying operations. The cave (Feldhofer grotto) was in Devonian limestone which formed the walls of the valley. Most of the valley no longer exists, neither does the cave. It is likely that much of the skeleton was lost before its significance was appreciated.

Associated finds
Neither artefacts nor fossil mammalian bones were found with the remains.

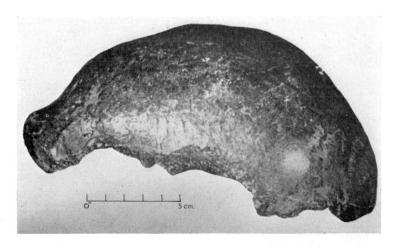

Fig. 19   The Neanderthal calotte
Courtesy of Professor J. S. Weiner

61

The Neanderthal Skeleton

Dating This find was perhaps the earliest acceptable example of fossil man, but because of the circumstances of the find, the lack of stratigraphy or associated tools and the absence of a fossil fauna it was impossible to date the skeleton with any confidence. It is likely that the man from Neanderthal died during the Fourth Glaciation (Würm or Last Glaciation).

Morphology The parts of the skeleton which have been preserved include the skull cap, one clavicle, one scapula, five ribs, two humeri, one radius, two ulnae, two femora and part of the pelvis.

THE CALOTTE

The vault of the skull is low, the supra-orbital ridges large and the occipital bone prominent. The sagittal suture and most of the coronal suture are obliterated, but the lambdoid suture is apparently still open. This degree of sutural fusion has led to the suggestion that the age at death was about 50 years.

THE POST-CRANIAL BONES

The limb bones are of rugged construction, having stout tuberosities and impressive muscular markings. The humeri are straight and cylindrical, but the radius is curved with an internal concavity. The radial tuberosity is very large, adumbrating a powerful biceps muscle. The left elbow was the site of an injury which severely limited movement at the joint. The femur is cylindrical and has the beginnings of a third trochanter.

Dimensions Hrdlička (1930)

THE CALOTTE

Length 201   Breadth 147

Cranial Index 73·1 (Dolichocephalic)

Cranial Capacity 1,033 cc (Schaafhausen, 1858)
1,230 cc (Huxley, 1863)
1,234 cc (Schwalbe)

POST-CRANIAL BONES

	Length	Mid-shaft diameter	
Humerus	312	26	
Femur	438	30	Schaafhausen, 1858
Radius	239	15·5	

Affinities The principal importance of this find is, perhaps, its historical interest, for in the years following *The Origin of Species* it caused intense controversy. Fuhlrott was willing to accept the antiquity of the bones and their contemporaneity with the mammoth, Virchow (1872) believed that the skull was pathological, whilst Blake (1864) considered that it belonged to an imbecile. Schaafhausen (1858) said that the bones were those of an ancient savage and barbarous race, but Huxley (1863) recognized the primitive features of the skeleton and could not accept that it was an intermediate form between man and apes; thus he proposed that Neanderthal man was an example of reversion towards a previous simian ancestor. King (1864) decided that the characters of the Neanderthal remains were so different from those of contemporary man that he proposed the name *Homo neanderthalensis*. The controversy continued unabated for many years until further finds convinced the sceptics that fossil man existed; of particular importance in this respect was the discovery of the La Chapelle-aux-Saints skeleton which shares numerous features with the Neanderthal remains. Boule was in no doubt that they were co-specific and declared the French find the type skeleton of the species; since then many Neanderthal skulls, skeletons and parts of skeletons have been found in Europe and the Near East as well as remains from Africa and Asia which are regarded by some anthropologists as being Neanderthaloid.

Original Rheinisches Landesmuseum, Bonn, West Germany.

Casts 1. F. Krantz, Rheinisches Mineralienkontor, Bonn, West Germany. (Calotte and post-cranial bones.)

2. The University Museum, University of Pennsylvania, Philadelphia 4, Pennsylvania, U.S.A. (Calotte and endocranial cast.)

References SCHAAFHAUSEN, H. 1858
Zur Kenntnis der ältesten Rassenschädel. *Archiv. Anat. Phys. wiss. Medicin*, pp. 453-478.
FUHLROTT, C. VON 1859
Menschliche Uebereste aus einer Felsengrotte des Düsselthals. *Verh. naturh. Ver. der preuss. Rheinl. 16*, 131-153.
HUXLEY, T. H. 1863
Evidence as to man's place in nature. London: Williams and Norgate.
KING, W. 1864
The reputed fossil man of the Neanderthal. *Quart. J. Sci. 1*, 88-97.
BLAKE, C. C. 1864
On the alleged peculiar characters and assumed antiquity of the human cranium from the Neanderthal. *J. anthrop. Soc. Lond. 2*, 139-157.

VIRCHOW, R. 1872
Untersuchung des Neanderthal-Schädels. *Z. Ethn. 4,* 157-165.
HRDLIČKA, A. 1930
The skeletal remains of early man. *Smithson. misc. Coll. 83,* 1-379
CAMPBELL, B. 1964
Quantitative taxonomy and human evolution. In *Classification and human evolution.* Ed. S. L. Washburn. pp. 50-74. London: Methuen and Co. Ltd.

The Mauer Mandible

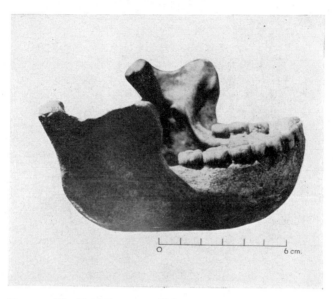

Fig. 20   The Heidelberg mandible
Courtesy of Dr R. Kraatz, Conservator, Geologisch-
Paläontologisches Institut der Universität, Heidelberg

Synonyms
and other names

Homo heidelbergensis (Schoetensack, 1908); *Palaeanthropus heidelbergensis* (Bonarelli, 1909a); Homo (Euranthropus) heidelbergensis (Arambourg, 1957)
Heidelberg man; Mauer man
Several other names have been proposed such as *Pseudhomo, Europanthropus* and *Rhenanthropus*. None has gained acceptance.

Site

The Rösch sandpit, half a mile north of the village of Mauer, three miles south of Neckargemund and about six miles south-east of Heidelberg, West Germany.

Found by

The mandible was found by a workman on the 21st October, 1907. It was shown to O. Schoetensack. (It is uncertain whether the fossil was seen *in situ* by Schoetensack.)

Geology

The deposits exposed at the pit consist of a lower series of river sands, the Mauer sands, from the bed of the Neckar   65 river. These sands are overlain by two layers of silt or loess which are approximately 50 feet thick and rest upon sandstone gravel. The mandible was found 80 feet from the surface, in the Mauer sands about 7 feet from the base of the layer.

Associated finds With the mandible was a well preserved fossil fauna of mammalian bones showing no evidence of water rolling. This fauna included Etruscan rhinoceros (*Didermocerus etruscus*), red deer (*Cervus elaphus*), straight-tusked elephant (*Palaeoloxodon antiquus*), bison (*Bison priscus*), moose (*Alces latifrons*), roe deer (*Capreolus capreolus*), horse (*Equus mosbachensis*), primitive bear (*Ursus sp.*) and beaver (*Castor fiber*). Less frequently there were carnivores including lion and primitive wolf.
No artefacts were found with the mandible.

Dating The fauna is post-Villafranchian and pre-Second Interglacial (Mindel–Riss or Penultimate Interglacial), suggesting that the climate was probably warm/temperate. The stratigraphy and fauna indicates that the Mauer sands were laid most probably during the First Interglacial or possibly during an interstadial within the Second Glaciation. Chemical or radiometric dating of the find is unknown. Kurtén (1962) places the Heidelberg mandible within the Second Glaciation, Oakley (1964) confidently attributes Heidelberg man to the First Interglacial period.

Morphology MANDIBLE
The mandible is large and stoutly built with broad ascending rami and rounded angles. The body is thick and particularly deep in the region of the premolars and molars; the mental symphysis is buttressed on its inner aspect but there is no simian shelf and no chin. The coronoid processes point forwards and laterally and the mandibular notches are shallow. The inner aspect of the bone shows well marked genial tubercles, and on each side a mylohyoid ridge above a shallow submandibular fossa. On the rami the openings of the inferior dental canals are overhung by lingular processes. On the left the groove for the mylohyoid nerve and vessels is particularly prominent.
Muscular markings include roughenings for the medial pterygoids, pits for the lateral pterygoids and marked inferior depressions for the digastric muscles. The mental foramina are 66

multiple (Howell, 1960). With the exception of those for the masseters, the muscular impresses are in keeping with the size of the bone.

TEETH

The dental arcade is parabolic and the tooth row has no diastema. The permanent dentition is complete although the premolars and first two molars of the left side are broken. The teeth appear small and probably lie within the crown dimension ranges of modern man; however, only the molars are said to lie within the range of size variation of the Choukoutien pithecanthropines. The molar cusp pattern is dryopithecine.

Molar Cusp Pattern (Howell, 1960)

	Lower Molars Left	Right
M1	Sub Y5	Sub Y5
M2	+ 5	+ 5
M3	+ 5	+ 5

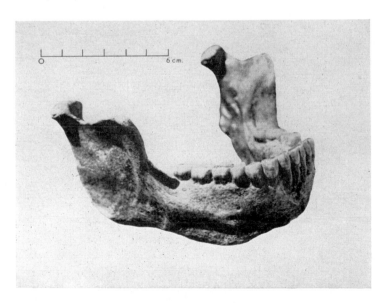

Fig. 21   The Heidelberg mandible
Courtesy of Dr R. Kraatz, Conservator, Geologisch-Paläontologisches Institut der Universität, Heidelberg

The Mauer Mandible

The molar teeth decrease in size in the order $M_2 > M_3 > M_1$, and all four are well worn. None of the molars has a cingulum or any sign of secondary enamel wrinkling. The premolars are bicuspid and the incisors somewhat swollen posteriorly, although not shovelled. The pulp cavities are moderately enlarged (taurodontism).

Dimensions

	Boule and Vallois (1957)	Wust (1951)	Howell (1960)
Symphysial Height	—	37·0	34·0
Body Height (Behind M1)	—	35·5 (M2)	34·3
Body Thickness	23·0 (M3)	19·5 (PM1)	22·0 (M1)
Ramus Height	66·0	69·0	71·0
Ramus Breadth	60·0	51·0	52·0
Mandibular angle	—	—	105°
Total Length	—	126·0	120·0
Bicondylar Breadth	—	130·0	133·0

TEETH
Howell (1960)

		Lower Teeth (Crown Dimensions)				
		PM1	PM2	M1	M2	M3
Left	l	7·3	—	11·1	12·9	11·5
Side	b	—	—	—	—	11·3
Right	l	8·1	7·5	11·6	12·7	12·2
Side	b	9·0	9·2	11·2	12·0	10·9

These figures broadly correspond to those of Schoetensack (1908), differing principally in terminology and in Howell's reluctance to measure broken teeth.

Affinities This is an important, but isolated, mandible whose morphology shows a number of points of similarity with the mandibles of pithecanthropines (*Homo erectus*) of approximately equivalent Middle Pleistocene age. The skull to which it belongs is unknown.

For many years the relationships of the jaw have been discussed because of its combination of relatively advanced teeth in a mandible which has such archaic features as a receding chin and broad rami. Recently Howell (1960) has reappraised the Mauer mandible and, concluding that its dental and mandibular morphology shows 'fundamental differences' from those of Java and Peking man, he tentatively suggests that Mauer man belongs to the lineage represented later by the

68

Montmaurin mandible and the early Neanderthalers. An alternative view places Mauer man within a larger group which could include the hominids from Java, Peking and Ternifine (Mayr, 1963). However, it has been suggested that the available material neither justifies the inclusion of Mauer man in any of the recently proposed subspecies of *Homo erectus*, nor warrants it being placed in a subspecific category of its own (Campbell, 1964).

Until the skull and/or the post-cranial bones are known, the affinities of this form must remain in doubt.

Original   Geologisch-Paläontologisches Institut der Universität, Heidelberg, West Germany.

Casts   1. F. Krantz, Rheinisches Mineralien-Kontor, Bonn, West Germany.

         2. The University Museum, University of Pennsylvania, Philadelphia 4, Pennsylvania, U.S.A.

References   SCHOETENSACK, O. 1908
Der Unterkiefer des Homo heidelbergensis *aus den Sanden von Mauer bei Heidelberg*, pp. 1-67. Leipzig: Wilhelm Englemann.
BONARELLI, G. 1909a
Palaeanthropus (n.g.) heidelbergensis (Schoet.) *Riv. ital. Palaeont. 15,* 26-31.
BONARELLI, G. 1909b
Le razze umane e le loro probabili affinita. *Boll. Soc. geog. ital. 10,* 827-851, 953-979.
WEINERT, H. 1937
Dem Unterkiefer von Mauer zur 30 jahrigen Wiederkehr seiner Entdeckung. *Z. Morph. Anthr. 37,* 102-113.
WUST, K. 1951
Üeber den Unterkiefer von Mauer (Heidelberg) im Vergleich zu anderen fossilen und mit besonderer Berucksichtigung der phyletischen Stellung des Heidelberger Fossils. *Z. Morph. Anthr. 42,* 1-112.
BOULE, M. and VALLOIS, H. V. 1957
Fossil men. London: Thames and Hudson.
ARAMBOURG, C. 1957
Les Pithécanthropiens, pp. 33-41. Brive: Melanges Pittard.
MAYR, E. 1963
Animal species and their evolution. London: Oxford University Press.
CAMPBELL, B. 1964
Quantitative taxonomy and human evolution. In *Classification and human evolution.* Ed. S. L. Washburn. London: Methuen and Co. Ltd., pp. 50-74.
OAKLEY, K. P. 1964
Frameworks for dating fossil man. London: Weidenfeld and Nicolson.   69

The Steinheim Calvarium

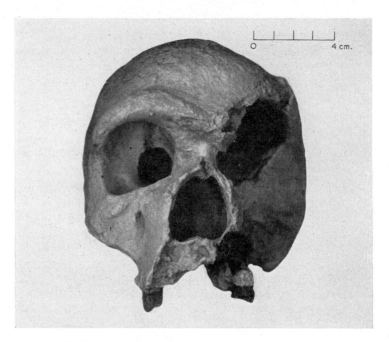

Fig. 22   The Steinheim skull (cast)
Frontal view

Synonyms   *Homo steinheimensis* (Berckhemer, 1936); *Homo (Protanthropus)* *steinheimensis* (Berckhemer, 1937); *Homo cf. sapiens* (Le Gros Clark, 1955); *Homo sapiens steinheimensis* (Campbell, 1964) Steinheim man

Site   The Sigrist gravel pit, Steinheim on the river Murr, about 12 miles north of Stuttgart, Wurttemberg, West Germany.

Found by   Karl Sigrist, Jun., 24th July, 1933. Unearthed by F. Berckhemer.

Geology   The calvarium was found in Pleistocene gravels washed down by the River Murr and deposited at Steinheim. The Sigrist pit shows several distinct strata of sands and gravels overlain by a layer of loess; these have been studied in detail by Berckhemer (1925) and others who demonstrated that the gravels are of two types and contain two separate faunal groups. This work has been continued and amplified by Adam (1954a and b) who

70

suggests that four layers can be distinguished, each characterized by its contained fauna, in particular by the elephant
remains.

Associated finds No artefacts have been recovered from the Steinheim gravels.
The layers have been named and characterized in the following
way:
1. *Younger Mammoth Gravels*
Containing steppe-mammoth (*Mammuthus primigenius*) and
woolly rhinoceros (*Coelodonta antiquitatis*).
2. *Main Mammoth Gravels*
Containing   steppe-mammoth   (*Mammuthus trogontherii-
primigenius*), bison (*Bison priscus*), horse (*Equus steinheimensis*)
and woolly rhinoceros (*Coelodonta antiquitatis*).
3. *Straight-tusked Elephant Gravels*
Containing straight-tusked elephant (*Palaeoloxodon antiquus*),
bear (*Ursus arctos*), wild ox (*Bos primigenius*) and lion (*Felis sp.*).
It was in this layer that Steinheim man was found.
4. *Older Mammoth Gravels*
Containing   steppe-mammoth   (*Mammuthus trogontherii*),
horse (*Equus cf. mosbachensis*), rhinoceros (*Didermocerus kirchbergensis*), bison (*Bison priscus*) and red deer (*Cervus elaphus*).
According to Adam (1954a) the fauna in gravel 3 is clear
evidence of an interglacial woodland environment at the time
the deposit was laid down, for the straight-tusked forest
elephant is almost confined to this layer whilst the steppe-
mammoth occurs in each of the other three layers.

Dating In the past opinion has varied regarding the dating of this find,
the gravels having been assigned by some to the Second
(Mindel–Riss) and by others to the Third (Riss–Würm)
Interglacials. In view of the evidence given above and other
evidence, Howell (1960) states that there can be no question
that the gravels in which the Steinheim calvarium was found
are other than of Second Interglacial age (Great, Mindel–Riss
or Penultimate Interglacial); this has been reaffirmed by
Kurtén (1962) and Oakley (1964).

Morphology CALVARIUM
A detailed description of the specimen has not yet been published, but several preliminary reports have appeared (Berckhemer, 1933 *et seq.*). A longer account was published by   71

Weinert (1946). The specimen, which is distorted and damaged, consists of the cranial and facial skeleton of a young
adult. The left orbit, temporal and infra-temporal regions
and part of the left maxilla are missing, as is the pre-maxillary
region of both sides. The base of the skull is broken away
around the foramen magnum, but it is well preserved in its
anterior portion. The upper right second premolar tooth and
all of the molar teeth are in place.

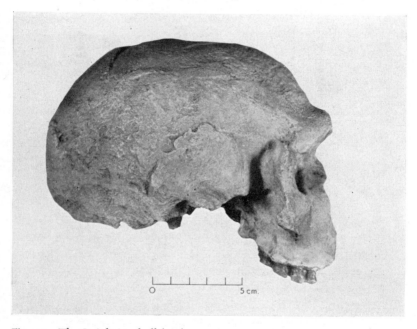

Fig. 23   The Steinheim skull (cast)
Right lateral view

The vault of the skull is long, narrow and moderately flattened;
the supra-orbital torus is pronounced, the nasal opening wide
and the root of the nose depressed. In lateral view the degree
of facial prognathism is small, the mastoid processes small but
well defined and the occipital region well rounded. There is
no occipital chignon but a low torus extends to the asterion.
The greatest width of the cranium is its biparietal diameter.

TEETH

The premolar crown is symmetrical but has a large buccal   72 cusp and a smaller lingual cusp. The molars decrease in size in the order $M1 > M2 > M3$. The third molar is markedly smaller than the other two and all are moderately taurodont.

Dimensions	CRANIUM	*Weinert* (1936)	*Howell* (1960)
	Length	184	185
	Breadth	132–133	116
	Cranial Index	72·0	62·5
	Cranial Capacity	1,070 cc	1,150–1,175 cc

Affinities The precise relationships of this form are uncertain as the morphological features of the specimen have never been fully compared with those of other hominids. Nevertheless, there is little doubt that the Steinheim calvarium has few similarities with the known *Homo erectus* skulls of the Middle Pleistocene, but it does share some features with the Neanderthalers such as the heavy supra-orbital torus and the broad nasal opening. Perhaps its principal resemblances are with the Swanscombe remains (*q.v.*) which have been attributed to *Homo sapiens*; for example in such features as the high position of the maximum breadth, the contour of the occiput and the form and thickness of the bones of the vault. The teeth are small and sapient in form and molar size order, but primitive in that they show a moderate degree of taurodontism although this feature is not unknown in modern populations.

One view of the position of Steinheim man is that he represents an intermediate stage between *Pithecanthropus* (*Homo erectus*) and later varieties of *Homo*, thus being ancestral to both Neanderthal and Modern man (Le Gros Clark, 1955). An alternative view (Weiner, 1958) does not accept Steinheim man as ancestral to the widely differing 'classic Neanderthaler' and modern man, but suggests that he represents a stage on a separate line leading to *Homo sapiens* and that Neanderthal and Rhodesian man have arisen from different and more primitive ancestors, for example Heidelberg, Montmaurin and Solo man.

It is likely that the evolutionary situation is more complicated than the earlier views would suggest, for it is possible that in the Middle Pleistocene a range of variable populations of early *Homo* were present, forms extending from pre-Neanderthal and pre-Rhodesian types to the more sapient groups represented by Steinheim and Swanscombe man (Weiner, 1958; Napier and Weiner, 1962).

Original Staatliches Museum für Naturkunde, Stuttgart, West Germany.

Casts 1. Staatliches Museum für Naturkunde, Stuttgart, West Germany. (Calvarium and reconstruction.)
2. The University Museum, University of Pennsylvania, Philadelphia 4, Pennsylvania, U.S.A. (Calvarium.)

References BERCKHEMER, F. 1925
Eine Riesenhirschstange aus den diluvialen Schottern von Steinheim a.d. Murr. *Jh. Ver. vater l. Naturk. Württemb. 81*, 99–108.
BERCKHEMER, F. 1933
Ein Menschen-Schädel aus den diluvialen Schottern von Steinheim a.d. Murr. *Anthrop. Anz. 10*, 318–321.
BERCKHEMER, F. 1936
Der Urmenschenschädel aus den zwischeneiszeitlichen Fluss— Schottern von Steinheim a.d. Murr. *Forsch. Fortsch. dtsch. Wiss. 12*, 349–350.
WEINERT, H. 1936
Der Urmenschenschädel von Steinheim. *Z. Morph. Anthr. 35*, 463–518.
BERCKHEMER, F. 1937
Bermerkungen zu H. Weinerts' Abhandlung 'Der Urmenschenschädel von Steinheim'. *Verh. Ges. phys. Anthrop. 2*, 49–58.
ADAM, K. D. 1954a
Die mittelpleistozänen Faunen von Steinheim an der Murr (Württemberg). *Quarternaria 1*, 131–144.
ADAM, K. D. 1954b
Die zeitliche Stellung der Urmenschen-Fundschicht von Steinheim an der Murr innerhalb des Pleistozäns. *Eiszeitalter Gegen. 4/5*, 18–21.
CLARK, W. E. LE GROS 1955
The fossil evidence for human evolution. Chicago: Chicago University Press.
WEINER, J. S. 1958
The pattern of evolutionary development of the genus *Homo. S. Afr. J. med. Sci. 23*, 111–120.
HOWELL, F. C. 1960
European and northwest African Middle Pleistocene hominids. *Curr. Anthrop. 1*, 195–232.
NAPIER, J. R., and WEINER, J. S. 1962
Olduvai Gorge and human origins. *Antiquity 36*, 41–47.
KURTÉN, B. 1962
The relative ages of the australopithecines of Transvaal and the pithecanthropines of Java. In *Evolution und Hominisation*. Ed. G. Kurth, pp. 74–80. Stuttgart: Gustav Fischer Verlag.

The Steinheim Calvarium

CAMPBELL, B. 1964
Quantitative taxonomy and human evolution. In *Classification and human evolution*. Ed. S. L. Washburn, pp. 50-74. London: Methuen and Co. Ltd.
OAKLEY, K. P. 1964
Frameworks for dating fossil man. London: Weidenfeld and Nicolson.

The Krapina Remains

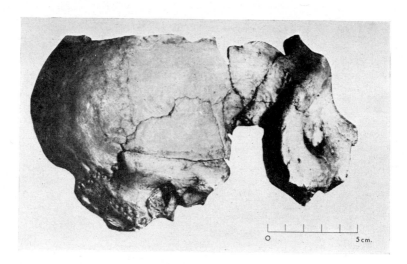

Fig. 24   The Krapina skull fragment
           Courtesy of Professor J. S. Weiner

Synonyms and other names
Homo primigenius var. krapinensis (Gorjanovič-Kramberger, 1906) Homo neandertalensis var. krapinensis (Skerlj, 1953)

Site
Near the river Krapinica, a tributary of the Drave, which runs through the small town of Krapina, 25 miles north-west of Zagreb, Yugoslavia.

Found by
K. Gorjanovič-Kramberger, September, 1899–July, 1905.

Geology
The remains were uncovered during the excavation of a rock shelter which had become filled by fallen debris. The deposit consisted of river sands overlain by the layer containing the remains; this in turn was covered by sand derived from the Miocene sandstone and conglomerate walls of the shelter. There was some evidence of fire in the deposit.

Associated finds
It is believed that large numbers of stone implements were recovered from the site but relatively few have been described; they appear to be of Mousterian type and include points and scrapers. In addition Acheulean and 'pre-Aurignacian' tools have been mentioned (Skerlj, 1953).

76

Fossil mammalian bones found at the site included those of Merck's rhinoceros (*Didermocerus mercki*), cave bear (*Ursus spelaeus*), wild ox (*Bos primigenius*), beaver (*Castor fiber*), marmot (*Marmotta marmotta*) and red deer (*Cervus elaphus*).

Dating   Originally the site was attributed to an early interglacial date, First or Second Interglacial (Günz–Mindel or Mindel–Riss); however, later authors have regarded the site as dating from late Third Interglacial or early Fourth Glaciation (Riss–Würm or Würm), e.g. Oakley (1964).

Morphology   The bones from Krapina are numerous but badly fragmented. They comprise the remains of at least 13 men, women and children; some of the bones show evidence of having been burned. Almost all the bones of the skeleton are represented, some several times, and many teeth.

SKULLS

Five skulls (A, B, C, D and E) are complete enough for study but only one (Skull C) gives any idea of the form of the cranium and face. This specimen consists of the upper part of the face together with part of the frontal bone, and the right temporal and parietal bones. It is probably the skull of an adolescent. The supra-orbital ridges—well marked laterally but divided in the midline—are separated by grooves from the somewhat retreating forehead. The bones of the vault are of modern form but the mastoid process is small. When reconstructed this skull was found to be brachycephalic.

The lower part of the Krapina face is represented by six maxillae (A–F) and nine mandibles (A–J, less I). These bones indicate that the palate was broad.

MANDIBLES

The most complete adult mandible (J) has a parabolic dental arcade bearing the permanent dentition, lacking only the first premolars and the left third molar. The body is relatively stout but there is no mandibular torus or simian shelf. The condyles are flattened, although this is probably due to osteo-arthritis of the temporo-mandibular joint. There is no chin but the beginnings of a sub-mental trigone is discernible. In some specimens the mental foramina are large and single, in others small and multiple.

THE TEETH

The Upper Incisors are moderately shovelled and several have basal 'finger-like' tubercles.

The Canines resemble those of modern man but some have ridged margins.

The Premolars are bicusped, symmetrical and taurodont.

The Molars have four or five cusps, well marked anterior foveae and, in unworn teeth, secondary wrinkling of the enamel. An upper left first molar has a distinct Carabelli cusp and pit, whilst both upper and lower third molars show some reduction in size. Taurodontism is extreme in these molar teeth.

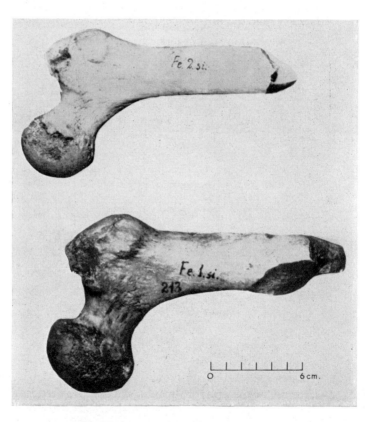

Fig. 25   The Krapina femoral heads
   Courtesy of Professor J. S. Weiner

POST-CRANIAL BONES

Amongst the large collection are vertebrae, ribs, clavicles, scapulae, humeri, radii, ulnae, hand bones; also innominate bones, femora, patellae, tibiae, a fibula, a calcaneum, tali and other foot bones. Many of the bones are broken and incomplete.

In general there is little to distinguish these bones from their counterparts in modern man. They do not display the coarse modelling, heavy muscular markings and large joints typical of the 'classic Neanderthaler', e.g. La Ferrassie, La Chapelle aux-Saints.

Dimensions (Selected from Gorjanovič-Kramberger, 1906)

SKULL C (Reconstructed)

Max. Length 178

Max. Breadth 149

Cranial Index 83·7 (Brachycephalic)

MANDIBLE J

Symphysial Height 42·3

Symphysial Thickness 15·0

Coronoid Height 73·0

Ramus Breadth (Middle) 37·0

TEETH

Lower Permanent Molars (Crown Dimensions)

Mandible J		M1	M2	M3
Left	l	11.0	12·5	—
Side	b	11·1	11·5	—
Right	l	11·4	11·5	11·6
Side	b	11·3	12·2	c 10·3

POST-CRANIAL BONES

Clavicle (complete)	Length	149·5 (adult)
Clavicle (complete)	Length	59·4 (child)
Capitate	Length	27·5
Capitate	Breadth	17·6
Innominate bone (left)	Acetabular dia.	53·5
Innominate bone (right)	Acetabular dia.	57·0
Femora	Mean dia. of head I	52·7
Femora	Mean dia. of head II	44·3
Talus	Length	53·3

Talus	Breadth	42·5
Talus	L/B Index	79·7
Cuboid	Length	37·5
Cuboid	Breadth	27·4

Numerous other measurements were given but many of them are of little value for comparative purposes since they are not standard dimensions.

Affinities   The relationships of the Krapina people are difficult to assess because the features of their skeletons are mixed. The skulls are somewhat archaic in that the supra-orbital torus is pronounced, the mastoid processes small and the palate broad; similarly the mandible is chinless. The teeth also have primitive traits such as the extreme taurodontism and wrinkled enamel, but none have cingula. On the other hand the post-cranial bones are modern in their principal features.

Recent opinion on the dating of these remains suggests that they probably antedate the 'classic Neanderthalers' of the Fourth Glaciation (Würm or Last Glaciation) and fall within the Third Interglacial (Riss–Würm or Last Interglacial).

For convenience these hominids have been termed 'generalized Neanderthalers', although not regarded as specifically distinct from *Homo sapiens*; however, there may be grounds for giving this group subspecific rank (Le Gros Clark, 1964). Even this distinction is doubtful since modern schemes of hominid taxonomy only allow 'classic Neanderthal' man subspecific status within *Homo sapiens* (Campbell, 1964).

Originals   National Museum of Geology and Palaeontology, Zagreb, Yugoslavia.

Casts   National Museum of Geology and Palaeontology, Zagreb, Yugoslavia (Cranio-facial fragment, two mandibles, one femur).

References   GORJANOVIĆ-KRAMBERGER, K. 1899
Vorläufige Mitteilung über den Krapinafund. *Mitt. anthrop. Ges. Wien 29*, 1, 65-68.
GORJANOVIĆ-KRAMBERGER, K. 1900
Der diluviale Mensch aus Krapina in Kroatien. *Mitt. anthrop. Ges. Wien 30*, 1, 203.
GORJANOVIĆ-KRAMBERGER, K. 1901-1905
Der paläolithische Mensch und seine Zeitgenossen aus dem Diluvium von Krapina in Kroatien. *Mitt. anthrop. Ges. Wien 31*, 164-197. *32*, 189-216. *34*, 187-199. *35*, 197-229.

GORJANOVIČ-KRAMBERGER, K. 1906
Der diluviale Mensch von Krapina in Kroatia. Ein Beitrag zur Paläo-anthropologie. Wiesbaden: C. W. Kreidels Verlag.

SKERLJ, B. 1953
In *Catalogue des hommes fossiles.* Eds. H. V. Vallois and H. L. Movius, Jnr. *C. R. Cong. geol. Internat. Algiers 1952.* Section 5, 250-251.

CLARK, W. E. LE GROS 1964
The fossil evidence for human evolution. 2nd Ed. p. 76. Chicago: Chicago University Press.

CAMPBELL, B. 1964
Quantitative taxonomy and human evolution. In *Classification and human evolution.* pp. 50-74. Ed. S. L. Washburn. London: Methuen and Co. Ltd.

OAKLEY, K. P. 1964
Frameworks for dating fossil man. p. 303. London: Weidenfeld and Nicolson.

81

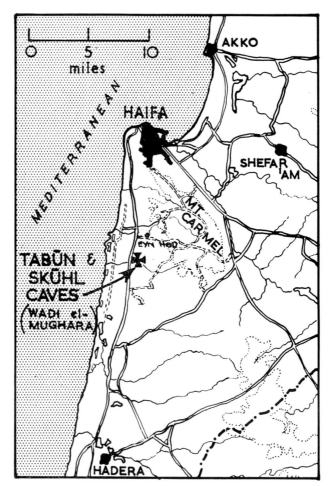

Fig. 26   The Tabūn and Skūhl sites

The Tabūn Remains

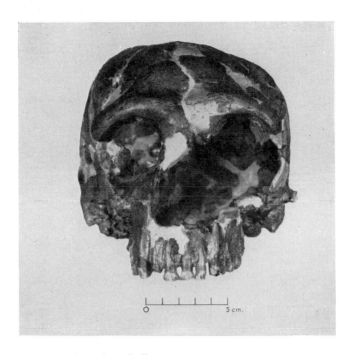

Fig. 27 The Tabūn skull
Frontal view
*Photographed by courtesy of the Trustees of the British
Museum (Nat. Hist.)*

Synonyms and other names	*Palaeoanthropus palestinensis* (McCown and Keith, 1939) Mount Carmel man
Site	Mugharet et-Tabūn, Wadi el-Mughara, Mount Carmel, south-east of Haifa, Israel.
Found by	Joint Expedition of the British School of Archaeology in Jerusalem and the American School of Prehistoric Research, directed by D. A. E. Garrod (1929–1934).
Geology	The western slope of Mount Carmel overlooking the Wadi el-Mughara is penetrated by a number of caves which are hollowed into a steep limestone escarpment. Excavation of the floor of the Tabūn cave disclosed a number of archaeological

83

layers characterized by the flint tools and fossil mammalian bones which they contained. During the excavation a female skeleton and a male mandible were uncovered as well as some other fragmentary hominid bones.

Associated finds The occupation levels were lettered A–G from above downwards, and contained several types of implements.

Uppermost layer—A	Iron age and recent artefacts.
Upper layers—B, C and D	Levalloiso-Mousterian flake tools.
Lower layers—E and F	Upper Acheulean hand axes, racloirs (scrapers), blades and retouched flakes (Yabrudian)
Lowermost layer—G	Tayacian tools, poor in quantity and quality.

The mammalian fossil fauna from layers C and D—the layers which contained the bulk of the hominid remains—was extensive and included hippopotamus (*Hippopotamus amphibius*), wild boar (*Sus gadarensis*), red deer (*Cervus elaphus*), fallow deer (*Dama dama mesopotamica*), wild ox (*Bos sp.*), gazelle (*Gazella sp.*), wild ass (*Equus hemionus*), hyena (*Crocuta crocuta*), rhinoceros (*Didermocerus cf. hemitoechus*) and roe deer (*Capreolus capreolus*). Above these layers, level B disclosed a distinct faunal break in that the fossil bones belonged to more modern forms, and the number of gazelle bones was much reduced whereas the fallow deer remains were increased. The new fauna did not contain hippopotamus, rhinoceros or other warm-climate species.

Dating Originally Garrod and Bate (1937) suggested that layers C and D belonged to the latter part of the Third Interglacial (Riss–Würm or Last Interglacial) and that the faunal break was evidence of the onset of the Würm Glaciation; however, carbon 14 dating of layer C at 45,000 ($\pm$2,000) years B.P. has altered this view. Recently (Garrod, 1962), has suggested that Tabūn C should be attributed to the second part of the Würm Glaciation and that the faunal break above this level was evidence of the onset of an interstadial period.

Morphology Tabūn I is an almost complete adult female skeleton aged about 30 years. Tabūn II is an isolated mandible believed to be male. In addition there are five other specimens of post- 84 cranial bones, at least some of which may belong to a further individual. The remains have been described in a lengthy monograph by Keith and McCown (1939).

TABŪN I

The skull was in fragments when found and needed extensive

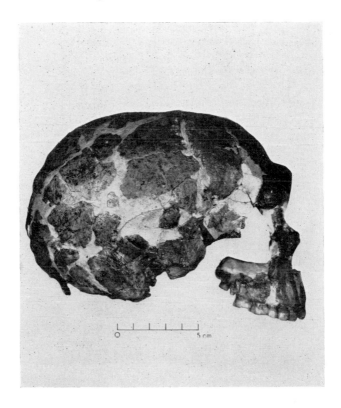

Fig. 28   The Tabūn skull
         Lateral view
         Photographed by courtesy of the Trustees of the British
         Museum (Nat. Hist.)

restoration. The cranium is small and low-vaulted with a pronounced frontal torus, and the outline of the skull from above is shaped so that its maximum breadth is towards the back. There is no marked 'bun-formation', but an occipital

85

torus denotes powerful nuchal muscles. The mastoid process is small. The face is orthognathous and appears to be bent backwards to lie beneath the skull base.

The mandible has a stout body, broad rami and widely separated condyles. The symphysis is oblique and there is no chin. The mental foramina are double.

TABŪN II

The second individual is represented by a robust mandible which has a broad ramus and a better-developed chin.

TEETH

Tabūn I has a complete dentition, except for lack of the upper right third molar. The incisors are worn but lingual tubercles are present on both incisors and canines. The premolars are not remarkable other than they have some buccal swelling of the crown. The first two molars have four-cusped square crowns with well marked oblique ridges, but the third molars are triangular, lacking hypocones. A Carabelli pit is present on the first and second upper molars but it is absent on the third upper molars. The Tabūn II mandible has very worn teeth but the lingual tubercles are less developed than those of Tabūn I. All the teeth are present in the Tabūn II mandible except for the left lateral incisor, and in general the crown morphology of the lower teeth of Tabūn I and II is similar. The isolated teeth have corresponding characteristics, the molars having a dryopithecine cusp pattern.

THE POST-CRANIAL BONES

The long bones of the Tabūn I skeleton tend to be short, robust and somewhat bowed. In particular the radius and ulna are stout and curved. The vertebral column is modern in form but the bones of the shoulder are stout with strong muscular markings reminiscent of the bones of the 'classic Neanderthalers'. The pelvic girdle is low and narrow with flattened pubic rami. The tibia has a somewhat retroverted head, otherwise it is of modern form.

Dimensions   *McCown and Keith* (1939)

TABŪN I SKULL

Max. Length 183   Max. Breadth 141
Cranial Index 77·0 (Mesocephalic)
Cranial Capacity 1,271 cc (Pearson's formula)

TABŪN I AND II MANDIBLES	Tabūn I	Tabūn II
Symphysial Angle	61°	72°
Bicondylar Width	(133)	(130)
Length	(95)	(119)

TEETH

		Upper Teeth (Crown Dimensions)						
Tabūn I	I1	I2	C	PM1	PM2	M1	M2	M3
l	9·0	7·3	7·9	7·5	6·5	10·8	10·5	8·3
b	8·2	7·7	8·8	9·8	9·6	11·5	11·7	10·2
Side	R	L	R	R	R	L	R	L

		Lower Teeth (Crown Dimensions)						
Tabūr I	I1	I2	C	PM1	PM2	M1	M2	M3
l	5·7	6·7	8·0	7·0	5·9	10·0	11·2	10·9
b	7·0	7·6	8·3	8·5	8·7	10·5	10·6	9·8
Side	R	R	R	R	R	R	R	L

		Lower Teeth (Crown Dimensions)						
Tabūn II	I1	I2	C	PM1	PM2	M1	M2	M3
Right l	5·9	6·1	8·0	7·8	7·9	11·0	10·8	11·5
Side b	8·0	8·2	9·0	9·0	9·5	11·0	11·0	10·8

TABŪN I POST-CRANIAL BONES

Length of Humerus	287	Left
Length of Radius	222	Left
Length of Ulna	243	Left
Length of Femur	(416)	Right
Length of Tibia	310	Left

( ) Approximate measurement

Affinities The Tabūn and Skūhl remains were found in separate caves literally within yards of each other. Both groups of bones were described by McCown and Keith (1939) in the same monograph. It is convenient to discuss their relationships together, despite the recent suggestion that chronologically they may be separated by 10,000 years (Higgs, 1961).

Originals *Tabūn I* and some isolated specimens from Layer C: British Museum (Natural History), Cromwell Road, South Kensington, London, S.W.7.

Tabūn II and some other fragments: Museum of the Department of Antiquities, Jerusalem.

The Tabūn Remains

The remaining specimens: Peabody Museum, Harvard University, Cambridge, Mass., U.S.A.

Casts   Tabūn II, mandible: The University Museum, University of Pennsylvania, Philadelphia 4, Pennsylvania, U.S.A.

References   GARROD, D. A. E., and BATE, D. M. A. 1937
The stone age of Mount Carmel. Col. 1   Excavations at the Wady el-Mughara. Oxford: The Clarendon Press.
McCOWN, T. D., and KEITH, A. 1939
The stone age of Mount Carmel. Vol. 2   The fossil human remains from the Levalloiso-Mousterian. Oxford: The Clarendon Press.
HIGGS, E. S. 1961
Some Pleistocene faunas of the Mediterranean coastal areas. *Proc. prehist. Soc. 27*, 144-154.
BROTHWELL, D. R. 1961
The people of Mount Carmel. *Proc. prehist. Soc. 27*, 155-159
HIGGS, E. S., and BROTHWELL, D. R. 1961
North Africa and Mount Carmel: Recent developments. *Man 61*, 138-139.
GARROD, D. A. E. 1962
The Middle Palaeolithic of the Near East and the problem of Mount Carmel man. *J. R. anthrop. Inst. 92*, 232-259.

The Skūhl Remains

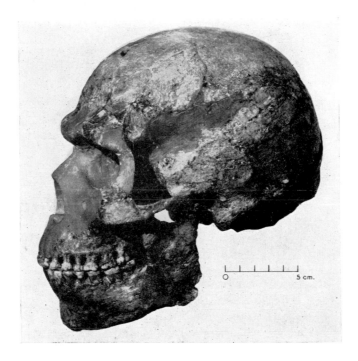

Fig. 29   The Skūhl V skull
Reconstructed by C. E. Snow
Left lateral view
Courtesy of the Trustees of the British Museum (Nat. Hist.)

Synonyms   *Palaeoanthropus palestinensis* (McCown and Keith, 1939)
and other names   Mount Carmel man

Site   Mugharet es-Skūhl, Wadi el-Mughara, Mount Carmel,
                    south-east of Haifa, Israel.

Found by   Joint expedition of the British School of Archaeology in
                    Jerusalem and the American School of Prehistoric Research,
                    directed by D. A. E. Garrod (1929–1934).

Geology   The western slope of Mount Carmel overlooking the Wadi
                    el-Mughara is penetrated by a number of caves which are
                    hollowed into a steep limestone escarpment. The smallest cave,
                    really a rock shelter, is the Mugharet es-Skūhl. Excavation   89

of the limestone breccia which formed the cave floor un-covered several archaeological layers containing flint tools and fossil mammalian bones. Amongst these remains there were a number of hominid bones, belonging to at least ten individuals who appeared to have been intentionally buried. Most of the bones were in proper relation with each other showing little sign of disturbance, but no grave furniture or grave outline was found. The only object directly related to the skeletons was a wild boar mandible in the arms of Skūhl V. Stratigraphi-cally the burials were all contemporaneous with the deposit.

Associated finds   The flint implements recovered from the cave all belong to the Levalloiso-Mousterian culture. No Acheulean tools precede them as in the Tabūn cave. The principal finds were made in layers B1 and B2 and consist of Mousterian points, racloirs (scrapers), Levallois flakes, cores and burins.

The fossil mammalian fauna included wild ox (*Bos sp.*), hyena (*Crocuta sp.*), hippopotamus (*Hippopotamus amphibius*), rhino-ceros (*Didermocerus cf. hemitoechus*), wild ass (*Equus hemionus*) gazelle (*Gazella sp.*), fallow deer (*Dama dama mesopotamica*), roe deer (*Capreolus capreolus*), red deer (*Cervus elaphus*), boar (*Sus gadarensis*) and small carnivores (*Felis sp.*). The wild ox was the commonest species in the assemblage.

Dating   The fauna of the Skūhl cave deposit can be correlated with the fauna of Tabūn layer C, prior to the faunal break of layer B. The tools found at the Tabūn and the Skūhl skeleton levels are almost indistinguishable in their workmanship; in view of this Garrod and Bate (1937) believed that the two sites were contemporaneous and could be attributed to the end of the Third Interglacial (Riss–Würm or Last Interglacial). By cor-relating the faunal changes found at several Mediterranean coastal sites, Higgs (1961) produced evidence which led him to suggest that the Skūhl site may be as much as 10,000 years more recent than the Tabūn site, and thus within the Gott-weiger Interstadial (Higgs and Brothwell, 1961). This view has been rejected by Garrod (1962) who maintains that the Tabūn and Skūhl remains are broadly contemporaneous, and quotes a tentative radiocarbon date of 45,000 ($\pm$2,000) years B.P. for layer C of Tabūn, thus within the second part of the Würm Glaciation.

Morphology The remains uncovered in the Skūhl cave have been identified by McCown and Keith (1939) as follows:

Designation	Status	Sex	Age in years	Bones
Skūhl I	Infant	? ♂	4–4½	Skeleton
Skūhl II	Adult	♀	30–40	Skeleton
Skūhl III	Adult	♂	—	Left leg bones
Skūhl IV	Adult	♂	40–50	Skeleton
Skūhl V	Adult	♂	30–40	Skeleton
Skūhl VI	Adult	♂	30–35	Skeleton
Skūhl VII	Adult	♀	35–40	Skeleton
Skūhl VIII	Child	? ♂	8–10	Lower limb bones
Skūhl IX	Adult	♂	Approx. 50	Incomplete skeleton
Skūhl X	Infant	? ♂	5–5½	Mandible and humeral fragment only

In addition there were sixteen isolated specimens.

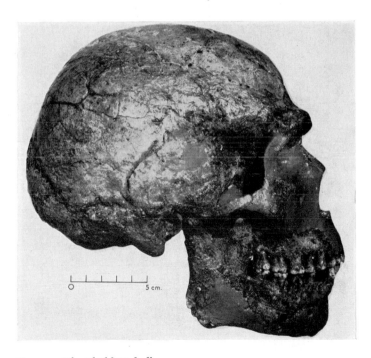

Fig. 30   The Skūhl V skull
Reconstructed by C. E. Snow
Right lateral view
Courtesy of the Trustees of the British Museum (Nat. Hist.)   91

SKULL

The best-preserved skull is that which belongs to Skūhl V. The cranial vault of this specimen is high, the supra-orbital torus marked and the occipital region full and rounded. The facial skeleton is somewhat prognathic and meets the vault at the depressed nasal root. The bony palate is broad but the temporomandibular joint and the mastoid process are of modern form. The external auditory meatus is tall but the greater wing of the sphenoid and the orbital process of the zygomatic bone have some archaic features. The angle of the cranial base (basispheniod/basioccipital angle) is modern, as is the plane of the foramen magnum.

TEETH

The teeth of the Skūhl specimens are worn but do not differ very much from the teeth of the Tabūn skull and mandible. Individual variation is discernible in that Skūhl VII has teeth with a few archaic features whereas Skūhl IV and V have more modern teeth. Skūhl V has bone evidence of dental sepsis in the form of several apical abcess cavities and the bony changes of pyorrhoea, but no dental caries.

MANDIBLE

In general the Skūhl mandibles have chins although this feature is poorly marked in Skūhl V. The mental foramina are single and the mandibular condyles do not differ appreciably from those of modern man, but some of the specimens have traits which recall the Tabūn mandibles.

POST-CRANIAL BONES

The post-cranial bones have mixed characteristics, the majority being very like those of modern man but others resembling those of the Tabūn skeleton. The Skūhl long bones are long and slender contrasting with the stout, curved and big-jointed bones of the so-called 'classic Neanderthaler'. The hands are large and broad with well developed thumbs. Similarly the feet are large, stoutly constructed and well arched, without doubt feet well adapted to a propulsive bipedal gait. The axial skeleton has few distinctive features but the fourth segment of the sternum of Skūhl IV is long and resembles that of the Tabūn skeleton. The ribs are variable in form, Skūhl V ribs having a thicker and more rounded cross-section than those of Skūhl IV which are flattened and modern.

Dimensions

McCown and Keith (1939)

SKULLS (Unrestored)	*Skūhl IV*	*Skūhl V*
Max. Length	(206)	192
Max. Breadth	(148)	143
Cranial Index	71·8	74·5
Cranial Capacity (Pearson's formula)	1,554 cc	1,518 cc

MANDIBLES

Bicondylar Width	(132)	(133)
Length	(118)	109
Symphysial Angle	75°	69°

POST-CRANIAL BONES	*Skūhl IV*	*Skūhl V*
Length of Humerus	—	Left 379
Length of Ulna	—	Right 270
Length of Radius	—	Right 236
Length of Femur	—	Right and Left (518)
Length of Tibia	—	Left (412)

TEETH

Skūhl V		I_1	I_2	C	PM_1	PM_2	M_1	M_2	M_3
Upper Teeth (Crown Dimensions)									
Right	l	8·5	7·0	8·7	8·2	7·0	11·0	10·8	9·1
Side	b	7·5	7·2	9·5	10·8	10·8	12·5	12·2	11·8

Skūhl V		I_1	I_2	C	PM_1	PM_2	M_1	M_2	M_3
Lower Teeth (Crown Dimensions)									
	l	5·0	6·4	8·0	8·2	7·7	11·3	11·6	11·4
	b	6·4	7·0	9·0	9·2	9·1	11·5	11·4	10·5
Side		L	R	R	L	R	R	R	R

( ) Approximate measurement

SKŪHL V (*Restored by C. E. Snow, 1953*)

SKULL	*Before restoration*	*After restoration*
Length	192	192
Breadth	143	144
Cranial Index	74·5	75·0
Cranial Capacity (Water displacement of cavity cast)	1,450 cc	—
(Pearson's formula)	1,518 cc	1,518 cc

MANDIBLE	*Before restoration*	*After restoration*
Length	109	107
Bicondylar Width	(132)	131
POST-CRANIAL BONES		
Humerus (Left)	379	378
Ulna (Right)	270	(280)
Radius (Right)	236	(254)
Femur (Right)	518	(505)
Tibia (Left)	412	(438)

( ) Approximate measurement

Affinities   At first McCown and Keith (1939) admitted that they believed the Tabūn and Skūhl remains to belong to two distinct peoples, but when their studies were completed they concluded that the burials represented a single population of one species or race, for three particular reasons. In the first place the dental characters of the two groups were uniform; secondly, the associated tool cultures were nearly identical; and, lastly, according to Garrod and Bate (1937) they were found at the same locality and were contemporaneous. None the less, anatomically the Skūhl skeletons were considered to be of a later type, representing one extreme of a variable series. McCown and Keith rejected the possibility of hybridity between Neanderthal and Cro-Magnon man as an explanation of the mixed characteristics of the Mount Carmel skeletons on the grounds that there were no known previous fossils of either of these groups in the vicinity; they suggested that the nearest relatives of Mount Carmel man were the Krapina people (*q.v.*) of approximately the same date. Subsequent authors were divided between 'extreme variability' and 'hybridization' as possible explanations for the morphological findings until Higgs (1961) cast doubt upon the dating of the Skūhl remains. The anthropological implications of the new dating were discussed by Brothwell (1961). He concluded that broadly the two groups of remains can be separated into an earlier Palestinian Neanderthal population (Tabūn) who were replaced by a more advanced sapient people (Skūhl), a concept supported by the evidence of the Djebel Kafzeh remains which are similar to those from Skūhl, and the remains from Gallilee and Shanidar which resemble the Tabūn specimen.   94

The Skūhl Remains

Originals Skūhl I and IV: Museum of the Department of Antiquities, Jerusalem.
Skūhl IX: British Museum (Natural History), Cromwell Road, South Kensington, London, S.W. 7.
Skūhl II, III, V, VI, VII, VIII and isolated teeth: Peabody Museum, Harvard University, Cambridge, Mass., U.S.A.

Casts Skūhl I, IV and V, also Skūhl V (C. E. Snow reconstruction): The University Museum, University of Pennsylvania, Philadelphia 4, Pennsylvania, U.S.A.

References GARROD, D. A. E., and BATE, D. M. A. 1937
The stone age of Mount Carmel. Vol. I Excavations at the Wady el-Mughara. Oxford: The Clarendon Press.
McCOWN, T. D., and KEITH, A. 1939
The stone age of Mount Carmel. Vol. II The fossil human remains from the Levalloiso-Mousterian. Oxford: The Clarendon Press.
SNOW, C. E. 1953
The Ancient Palestinian Skūhl V reconstruction. Amer. Sch. prehist. Res. Bull. 17, 5-12.
HIGGS, E. S. 1961
Some Pleistocene faunas of the Mediterranean coastal areas. Proc. prehist. Soc. 27, 144-154.
BROTHWELL, D. R. 1961
The people of Mount Carmel. Proc. prehist. Soc. 27, 155-159.
HIGGS, E. S., and BROTHWELL, D. R. 1961
North Africa and Mount Carmel: Recent developments. Man 61, 138-139.
GARROD, D. A. E. 1962
The Middle Palaeolithic of the Near East and the problem of Mount Carmel man. J. R. anthrop. Inst. 92, 232-259.

The Tell Ubeidiya Remains

Synonyms and other names	Jordan man
Site	Near Tell Ubeidiya, west of Kibbutz Beit Zera on the western slope of the Jordan valley, about two miles from the Jordan outlet of Lake Tiberias, Israel.
Found by	Y. Merinsky, June, 1959. Recognized by G. Haas.
Geology	The remains were found when a field was being levelled by a bulldozer. The locality in which the material was found was surveyed in 1930–1931 by L. Picard; the bones were un-covered from Pleistocene freshwater lake and river deposits, termed the '*Melanopsis*' stage, which have outcropped follow-ing major faulting of the underlying strata (Stekelis *et al.*, 1960). The local stratigraphy has been described in detail, in the same publication, following the excavation of a trench at the site of the find.
Associated finds	With the bones were some primitive stone tools made from water-worn pebbles of various sizes. The types of implement found include roughly trimmed stone balls, 'chopping tools' made by striking two flakes from one side of a pebble, elongated trihedral points made of flint and some flakes which may have been utilized. Several animal bones were recovered which have been split and marked by cuts indicating that the flesh may have been removed with flint implements. One split bone is alleged to have a smooth edge suggesting that it had been used as a tool. The vertebrate fossil fauna, provisionally determined, included freshwater turtle (*Trionyx sp.*), hippopotamus (*Hippopotamus sp.*), horse (*Equus sp.*), rhinoceros and several proboscidians amongst many other forms listed.
Dating	The fauna of the '*Melanopsis*' stage, as provisionally deter-mined, has suggested a Villafranchian (Lower Pleistocene) date for this deposit. However, Hooijer (1962) has expressed doubts that the published faunal list will prove compatible with a Villafranchian age and suggests that it may be a Middle Pleistocene assemblage.

The Tell Ubeidiya Remains

Morphology The hominid remains from Ubeidiya are scanty and com-
minuted, consisting of two skull fragments and an incisor
tooth. No description of these remains is available at present
but it has been stated that the vault is of very great thickness.
Brief examination of the remains can add little other than that
the incisor is worn and not markedly shovelled.

Affinities Until the bones have been described any attempt at classification must be speculative, but their features do not seem to
exclude the possibility that they belonged to *Homo erectus*.

Originals The Hebrew University of Jerusalem, Israel.

Casts Not available at present.

References STEKELIS, M., PICARD, L., SCHULMAN, N., and HAAS, G. 1960
Villafranchian deposits near Ubeidiya in the Central Jordan Valley
(Preliminary report). *Bull. Res. Coun. Israel* 9G, 175-184.
HOOIJER, D. A. 1962
The Middle Pleistocene fauna of the Near East. In *Evolution und
Hominisation*. Ed. G. Kurth, pp. 81-83. Stuttgart: Gustav Fischer
Verlag.

97

HFM

North-west Africa

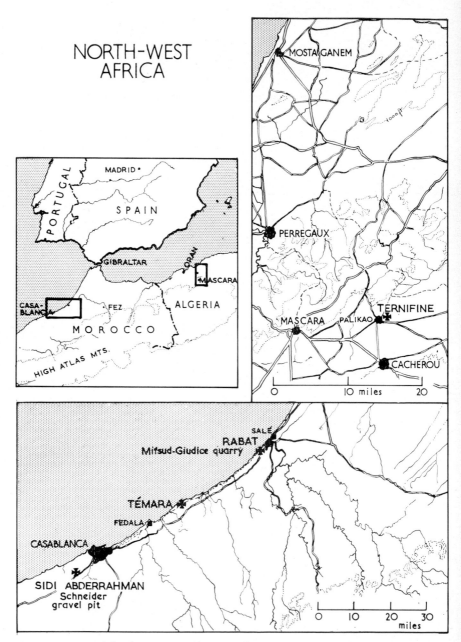

Fig. 31   Hominid fossil sites in North-west Africa

The Ternifine Remains

Synonyms and other names   *Atlanthropus mauritanicus* (Arambourg, 1954)
Ternifine man

Site   Ternifine, near the village of Palikao, 11 miles east of Mascara, Oran, Algeria.

Found by   C. Arambourg and R. Hoffstetter, July, 1954; C. Arambourg, 1955.

Geology   Commercial excavation of a large hill of sand exposed the bed of a Pleistocene artesian lake containing fossil bones and stone tools. The level of the water table made it necessary for pumps to be used in the recent exposure of the lower layers.

Associated finds   Several hundred implements were recovered from the site, made principally of quartzite and sandstone but occasionally of poor-quality flint. The tools included primitive biface hand-axes, scrapers and a type of small axe with a curved blade; an industry described as Acheuléen II (Balout and Tixier, 1957). The associated fossil fauna was rich and varied containing many extinct forms suggestive of a tropical savannah environment. The predominant mammals were hippopotamus (*Hippopotamus amphibius*), elephant (*Loxodonta atlantica*), early zebra (*Equus mauritanicus*), rhinoceros (*Ceratotherium simum-mauritanicum*), camel (*Camelus thomasi*), several antelopes and numerous carnivores. In addition, several species of particular importance were identified, a sabre-toothed cat (*Homotherium latidens*), giant wart-hog (*Afrochoerus sp.*) and a giant baboon (*cf. Simopithecus*).

Dating   The character of the fauna, especially the presence of the last three species, in conjunction with the type of industry, allowed Arambourg (1955a) to establish an early Middle Pleistocene date for these deposits.

Morphology   Arambourg (1963)
The hominid bones which were discovered comprise three mandibles and a parietal bone.

MANDIBLES
The mandibles are all adult and remarkable for their size and robustness. Nos. I and III are probably male, whereas No. II despite its great size is probably female. In all three specimens

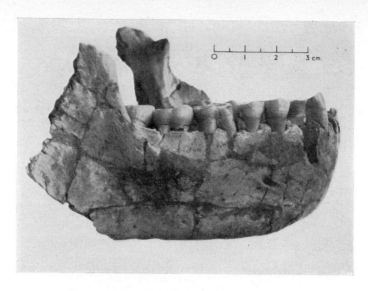

Fig. 32   The Ternifine I mandible
           Right lateral view
           Courtesy of Professor C. Arambourg

Fig. 33   The Ternifine I mandible
           Occlusal view
           Courtesy of Professor C. Arambourg

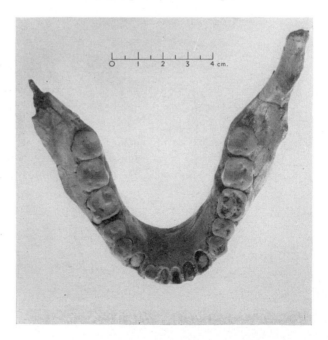

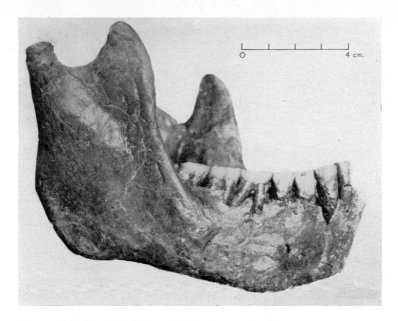

Fig. 34   The Ternifine III mandible
          Right lateral view
          Courtesy of Professor C. Arambourg

Fig. 35   The Ternifine III mandible
          Occlusal view
          Courtesy of Professor C. Arambourg

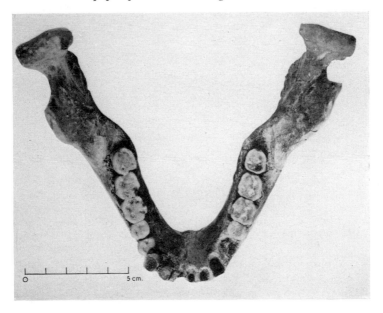

the borders of the bodies of the mandibles are parallel, the symphyses slope backwards, so that there are no chins, but a sub-mental trigone is present in Nos. II and III. The dental arcades are parabolic and there are several mental foramina in Nos. I and III. The body of No. I is strengthened by a prominent marginal torus. The rami are broken, but enough remains to suggest some variability; none the less they are all broad with marked impresses for masseter and medial pterygoid muscles.

TEETH

The incisors and canines are known only from the two worn specimens present in No. III. Little more can be said than that they appear hominid. The premolars are large, the first having an asymmetrical crown with a prominent buccal cusp and a smaller lingual cusp more distally placed. The second premolars have large buccal and lingual cusps placed opposite to each other, and large posterior fovea. The premolar teeth have large labial cingula whilst the second premolar, which is little worn, shows marked secondary enamel wrinkling.

The molar teeth are large and decrease in size in the order

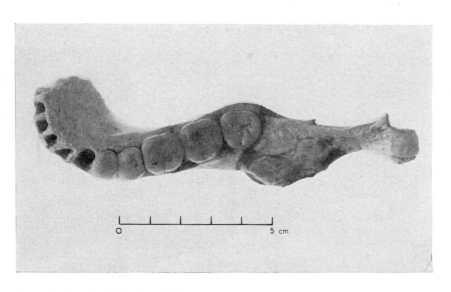

Fig. 36   The Ternifine II mandible
Courtesy of Professor C. Arambourg

M2 > M1 > M3. The cusp pattern is dryopithecine (Y5 or + 5), sixth cusps being present in No. II (M2, M3) and No. III (? M3) (Howell, 1960). It is probable that secondary enamel wrinkling was present on the occlusal surfaces of the molars as shown by those which are least worn; signs of a buccal cingulum are present on some of the molar teeth.

THE PARIETAL (Arambourg, 1955c)

The parietal is young, for all its sutures were open at the time of death. Its thickness is within the range of variation found in modern man. The parietal curve indicates that the vault was probably low and that the widest diameter of the cranium was bitemporal rather than biparietal. The temporal lines are well inscribed and testify to the power of the temporalis muscle. Internally the bone is heaped to form a prominent Sylvian crest whilst the middle meningeal pattern is primitive in its design, the principal division of the vessel having occurred before it reached the parietal bone. Thereafter, the anterior and bregmatic branches are weak but the temporal branch is stronger.

Dimensions *Arambourg* (1955b) *and Howell* (1960)

Mandibles	No. I	No. II	No. III
Symphysial height	39	35	39
Body height (Behind M1)	35	34	38
Body thickness (Behind M1)	19	16	20
Ramus height	—	72	93
Ramus breadth	—	45	48
Mandibular angle	—	98°	111°
Total length	110	110	129
Bicondylar breadth	—	—	158

Mandibles		Lower Teeth (Crown Dimensions)	
	No. I	No. II	No. III
PM1 l	8·5	9·0	8·0
b	9·0	11·2	10·0
PM2 l	8·0	9·5	8·2
b	10·0	10·5	10·0
M1 l	12·8	14·0	12·0
b	12·0	13·0	11·8
M2 l	13·0	14·2	12·0
b	13·7	13·7	12·1
M3 l	12·0	13·2	8·0
b	12·5	12·5	11·5

Affinities　The similarities between the Ternifine mandibles and those of Choukoutien Locality I (*Homo erectus*) are particularly striking. Features such as the mandibular torus, the shape of the dental arcade and the mental trigone, the form of the first premolar, the molar size order, the enamel wrinkling and the presence of cingular ridges, all argue for their morphological relationship. These likenesses were recognized by Arambourg (1954), but the Ternifine remains have been provisionally named *Atlanthropus mauritanicus* until more is known of these African representatives of the pithecanthropines of the Far East. Howell (1960) also accepted the resemblances between the Ternifine and Choukoutien mandibles and asserted that 'there are no differences between the Ternifine and Choukoutien Locality I people which might not be expected within a single polytypic species, populations of which were widely separated geographically'.

Originals　Institute de Paléontologie, 8, Rue de Buffon, Paris–5ᵉ, France.

Casts　Not generally available at present.

References　ARAMBOURG, C., and HOFFSTETTER, R. 1954
Découverte, en Afrique du Nord, de restes humains du Paléolithic inférieur. *C. R. Acad. Sci. Paris 239*, 72–74.
ARAMBOURG, C. 1954
L'hominien fossile de Ternifine (Algérie). *C. R. Acad. Sci. Paris 239*, 893–895.
ARAMBOURG, C. 1955a
A recent discovery in human paleontology: *Atlanthropus* of Ternifine (Algeria). *Am. J. Phys. Anthrop. 13*, 191–202.
ARAMBOURG, C. 1955b
Une nouvelle mandibule 'd'Atlanthropus' au gisement de Ternifine. *C. R. Acad. Sci. Paris. 241*, 895–897.
ARAMBOURG, C. 1955c
Le pariétal de l'*Atlanthropus mauritanicus*. *C. R. Acad. Sci. Paris 241*, 980–982.
ARAMBOURG, C. 1956
Une IIIᵉᵐᵉ mandibule d' '*Atlanthropus*' découverte à Ternifine. *Quarternaria 3*, 1–4.
BALOUT, L., and TIXIER, J. 1957
L'Acheuléen de Ternifine. *C. R. Congr. préhist. Fr. XVᵉ, 1956*, pp. 214–218.
HOWELL, F. C. 1960
European and northwest African Middle Pleistocene hominids. *Curr. Anthrop. 1*, 195–232.
ARAMBOURG, C. 1963
Le gisement de Ternifine. Part I C. Arambourg and R. Hoffstetter, Part II C. Arambourg. *Archs Inst. Paléont. hum. 32*, 1–190.

The Casablanca Mandible

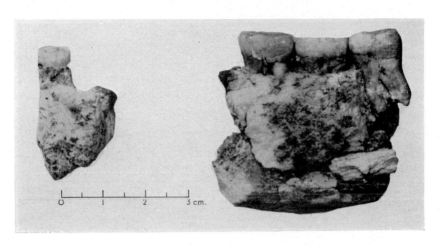

Fig. 37   The Casablanca mandibular fragments
        Courtesy of Professor C. Arambourg

Synonyms *Atlanthropus mauritanicus* (Arambourg and Biberson, 1956)
and other names Casablanca man : Littorina Cave man

Site The Schneider gravel pit at Sidi Abderrahman, about four
and a half miles south-west of Casablanca, Morocco, North
Africa.

Found by P. Biberson, 1954.

Geology The deposits at Sidi Abderrahman consist of Pleistocene sands
and gravels resting upon a pre-Pleistocene substratum of
Cambrian quartzites and calcareous clays. Above this are
several layers of conglomerate and beach sands, which separate the basal strata from the overlying 'Great Dune' calcareous
sandstone bed. This dune was attacked by the sea and karstic
caves were created in the sandstone cliff. Subsequently these
caves were filled by marine deposits. The Casablanca jaw was
found at the base of the cliff in a lens of marine sandstone.
The stratigraphy of this region has been described in detail by
Biberson (Biberson, 1955; Arambourg and Biberson, 1956;
Biberson, 1956).

Associated finds An abundance of stone implements of varying degrees of   107 workmanship were found in these deposits, but the tools associated with the remains were flattened biface hand-axes of the Middle Acheulean culture (Middle Acheulean II).

The fauna recovered from the near-by series of deposits includes elephant (*Loxodonta jolensis*), rhinoceros (*Cerato-therium simum*), early zebra (*Equus mauritanicus*), hippopotamus (*Hippopotamus amphibius*), several antelopes and gazelles as well as wild boar (*Sus scrofa*) and wild ox (*Bos primigenius*).

Dating   The detailed stratigraphy mapped by Biberson led him to attribute the find to the rise in sea level which corresponds to the beginning of the North African Third Pluvial; this prob-ably equates with the European Third Glaciation (Riss or Penultimate Glaciation) of the Upper Middle Pleistocene.

Morphology   Two fragments of an adult hominid mandible were found. The main specimen is the posterior part of the right side of the body and bears three molar teeth; the smaller fragment is part of the left side of the body behind the symphysis and has the first premolar in place.

THE MANDIBLE

The body of the mandible is robust but shows no mandibular torus. The parallel alveolar and ventral borders give no indica-tion of the formation of a chin, and the obliquity of the labial surface at the level of the second incisor suggests that the symphysis was retreating.

THE TEETH

The teeth are undoubtedly hominid and are heavily worn. The first premolar has traces of a cingulum and the crown of the tooth is asymmetrical. The molars are large, decreasing in size in the order $M2 > M1 > M3$; the third molar has secondary enamel wrinkling of the unworn part of its occlusal surface and all three have signs of a cingulum. The five cusps are arranged in the Y pattern and the third molar, despite its wear, has a sixth cusp.

Dimensions   *Arambourg and Biberson* (1955 and 1956)

MANDIBLE

Height at M1 35.0	Thickness at M1 17.3
Height at M2 34.5	Thickness at M2 17.0
Length of molar series 39·3	Robusticity Index 49·4

                                      (Vallois and Roche, 1958)

TEETH

	Lower Teeth (Crown Dimensions)			
	PM1	M1	M2	M3
Length	9·0	13·0	14·0	12·2
Breadth	9·6	11·6	11·2	11·3
Side	L	R	R	R

Affinities It seems clear that the Casablanca mandible belonged to a form closely related to *Atlanthropus* and probably therefore to the pithecanthropines of the Far East (Arambourg and Biberson, 1955, 1956; Howell, 1960). The features of the teeth recall *Pithecanthropus* and *Sinanthropus* (*Homo erectus*), and differ from them only in minor features which may well be within the range of normal variation of this group.

Originals Institut de Paléontologie, 8, Rue de Buffon, Paris–5ᵉ, France.

Casts Not generally available at present.

References ARAMBOURG, C., and BIBERSON, P. 1955
Découverte de vestiges humains acheuléens dans la carrière de Sidi Abd-er-rahman, près Casablanca. *C. R. Acad. Sci. Paris 240*, 1661-1663.
BIBERSON, P. 1955
Nouvelles observations sur le Quarternaire côtier de la région de Casablanca (Maroc). *Quarternaria 2*, 109-149.
ARAMBOURG, C., and BIBERSON, P. 1956
The fossil human remains from the Paleolithic site of Side Abderrahman (Morocco). *Am. J. Phys. Anthrop. 14*, 467-490.
BIBERSON, P. 1956
Le gisement de l'Atlanthrope de Sidi Abderrahman (Casablanca). *Bull. Archéol. Maroc 56*, 37-92.
VALLOIS, H. V., and ROCHE, J. 1958
La mandibule Acheuléene de Témara Maroc. *C. R. Acad. Sci. Paris 246*, 3113-3116.
HOWELL, F. C. 1960
European and northwest African Middle Pleistocene hominids. *Curr. Anthrop. 1*, 195-232.

The Rabat Mandible

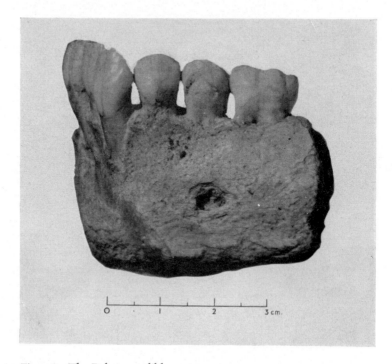

Fig. 38   The Rabat mandible
Courtesy of Professor C. Arambourg

Synonyms   Rabat man
and other names

Site   The Mifsud-Giudice quarry, near the Marie-Feuillet Hospital immediately south of Rabat, Morocco.

Found by   Workmen, then by J. Marçais, 3rd February, 1933.

Geology   The quarry is cut into the 'Great Dune' sandstone from the coast, where the exposed strata show alternations of consolidated calcareous sandstone and marine deposits. The Rabat remains were found in the sandstone during blasting. It is likely that the whole skull was present, as many small fragments of bone were recovered as well as the mandible and maxilla.

Associated finds   No stone tools or fossil mammalian bones were recovered   110 with the mandible, but the deposits have yielded a fauna which includes rhinoceros (*Ceratotherium simum*), early zebra (*Equus mauritanicus*), hyena (*Crocuta crocuta*), hippopotamus (*Hippopotamus amphibius*) and hartebeest (*Alcelaphus boselaphus*)—a typically tropical African assemblage.

Dating   The stratigraphy of this region is complex and has been investigated by a number of workers whose opinions vary as to the exact date of the site within the Middle Pleistocene. Recently Howell (1960) suggested that the Rabat remains are broadly contemporaneous with the Casablanca mandible, i.e. Upper Middle Pleistocene.

Morphology   The fragments probably belonged to an adolescent male of about 16 or 17 years of age. The principal specimens are part of a left maxilla and the major part of the body of a mandible, both fragments bearing teeth.

THE MAXILLA

The canine fossa is feebly developed and there is some degree of alveolar prognathism, but the palate is large and broader than that of modern man. The maxilla has in place two incisors, a canine, two premolars and two molars; the third molar is about to erupt.

THE MANDIBLE

The mandible is robust and has no chin. Internally it is strengthened by a strong transverse crest beneath which the inferior genial tubercles join in the midline. The digastric impressions are placed ventrally but are poorly limited. The mental foramina are double on the right side. The mandible contains three incisors, two canines, four premolars and the left first and the right third molars; the roots of the right first and second molars are also present.

THE TEETH

The upper incisors are shovelled whilst the canine is large and projects above the occlusal plane; this tooth has a marked buccal cingulum. The upper premolars have complex cusps and cingula recalling the pattern of the Choukoutien Locality I premolars. The molars both have cingula and the crown of M2 is larger than that of M1.

The lower teeth, anterior to the canines, are arranged in a transverse row and the canines themselves are chisel-edged, resembling incisors. The first lower premolar has an asymmetrical crown and a prominent lingual cusp; the second lower premolar is double-rooted and has a prominent talonid. The molars are large, each with signs of a buccal cingulum and enlarged pulp cavities (taurodontism). The cusp pattern is dryopithecine, of the Y_5 (M_1) or $+_5$ (M_2) variety.

Dimensions MANDIBLE

Vallois (1945)
Body Thickness (at mental foramen) 18
Symphysial Angle 98°
Robusticity Index 55·5 (Vallois and Roche, 1958)
Symphysial Angle (to the alveolar plane) 65° (Vallois and Roche, 1958)

TEETH

Vallois (1958–1959)

		Permanent Teeth (Crown Dimensions)							
		I_1	I_2	C	PM_1	PM_2	M_1	M_2	M_3
Upper	l	—	8·0	9·5	8·5	8·0	12·0	11·5	—
Teeth	b	—	8·5	10·0	(12·0)	11·0	12·0	13·0	—
Lower	l	6·0	7·0	8·5	9·0	9·0	12·0	—	12·5
Teeth	b	7·0	7·5	9·5	10·0	9·5	11·0	—	11·0

( ) Estimated

Affinities Following an examination of the material, Vallois (1945, 1958–1959) concluded that the remains have a number of primitive features which resemble those of the Neanderthalers; however some characters were nearer those of *Sinanthropus*. In consequence he suggested that Rabat man was a Neanderthaler, but more archaic than those of Europe. Howell (1960) asserts that the Rabat remains are of the same Middle Pleistocene group as the Casablanca specimen and that both are closely related to the earlier Ternifine population. Arambourg (1962) has stated that Rabat man is a young *Atlanthropus* and has all the dental characters of the pithecanthropines.

Originals Institut de Paléontologie humaine, Rue René Panhard, Paris.

Casts Not generally available at present.

References MARÇAIS, J. 1934
Découverte de restes humains fossiles dans le grès Quarternaires de Rabat (Maroc). *Anthropologie* 44, 579–583.

VALLOIS, H. V. 1945
L'homme fossile de Rabat. *C. R. Acad. Sci. Paris 221*, 669–671.

VALLOIS, H. V., and ROCHE, J. 1958
La mandibule Acheuléene de Témara Maroc. *C. R. Acad. Sci. Paris 246*, 3113–3116.

VALLOIS, H. V. 1958–1959
L'homme de Rabat. *Bull. Archéol. Maroc 3*, 87–91.

HOWELL, F. C. 1960
European and northwest African Middle Pleistocene hominids. *Curr. Anthrop. 1*, 195–232.

ARAMBOURG, C. 1962
In 'A re-examination of the Kanam mandible'. P. V. Tobias, pp. 341–360 (p. 359). *Proc. Fourth Pan-African Cong. Prehist. Leopoldville, 1959.* Tervuren: Musée Royal de l'Afrique Centrale.

The Témara Mandible

Synonyms and other names	The Témara mandible (Vallois and Roche, 1958)
Site	Témara, about 11 miles south-west of Rabat, Morocco.
Found by	J. Roche, ?1958.
Geology	The mandible was found in the 'Smugglers' Cave' on the coast of Morocco. On the walls of the cave were plaques of a former cave-filling which has been removed by the sea; one of these plaques contained the mandible.
Associated finds	The artefacts found with the mandible are said to be of Upper Acheulean type. The associated fauna, if any, is not known at present.
Dating	The breccia is said to date from the beginning of the last North African Pluvial, or just before, and corresponds with the Upper Acheulean cultural phase.
Morphology	*Vallois and Roche* (1958) The specimen consists of almost all of the body and two-thirds of the left ramus of a hominid mandible, with two fragments of the right ramus. All of the molar teeth are present, also representatives of the premolars and canines.

THE MANDIBLE

The mandible is stoutly built, but its general dimensions are said to be near the mean of those of modern man. The thickness of the body differs from modern mandibles in that the Témara jaw is stoutest in the region of the symphysis and the third molar, whereas modern mandibles tend to be stoutest between these two points.

The symphysis does not recede markedly and the digastric impressions extend only to the first premolar teeth. Internally there are no sublingual fossae but there is a ridge below the mylohyoid line. The ramus is large and low with a rounded gonial angle, and the mandibular notch is shallow.

TEETH

The teeth are robust. The canine is large and chisel-edged having a trilobed vestibular surface. The first premolar has an intercuspid bridge whilst the second is molariform and appears quadrituberculate. The molars diminish in size in the order

The Témara Mandible

$M_1 > M_2 > M_3$. The right third molar is damaged. The molar cusp pattern is dryopithecine (Y_5) with the exception of the first molar which has a + pattern. The metaconids are larger than the protoconids; all the molars have hypoconulids and the left third molar has a feeble sixth cusp. The pulp cavities are enlarged (taurodontism).

Dimensions MANDIBLE
Robusticity Index 53·7
Symphysial Angle (from the alveolar plane) 76°
TEETH
Premolar/Molar Series Length 55·0
No other dimensions are available at present.

Affinities As only a brief preliminary report has appeared on this mandible it is impossible to assess its relationships fully. It appears to be a robust mandible with a primitive symphysis, broad rami and large, somewhat archaic teeth; not unlike the other North African mandibles which have been attributed to *Atlanthropus* (*Homo erectus*). Vallois and Roche (1958) have stated that the jaw belongs to the pre-Neanderthalians, forms parallel with, but not identical to, Steinheim and Montmaurin man in Europe.

Original Institute de Paléontologie humaine, Rue René Panhard, Paris.

Casts Not available at present.

References VALLOIS, H. V., and ROCHE, J. 1958
La Mandibule Acheuléene de Témara Maroc. *C. R. Acad. Sci. Paris* *246*, 3113–3116.

East and Central Africa

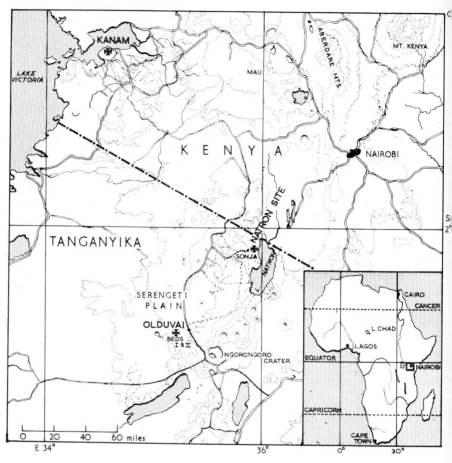

Fig. 39 Hominid fossil sites in East Africa

The 'Zinjanthropus' Remains from Bed I

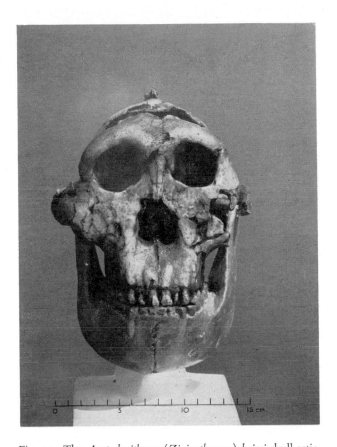

Fig. 40   The *Australopithecus* (*Zinjanthropus*) *boisei* skull artic-
ulated with a modified Natron mandible
Frontal view
*Courtesy of Dr L. S. B. Leakey and Bob Campbell,
Armand Denis Productions*

*Synonyms
and other names*   *Zinjanthropus boisei* (Leakey, 1959); *Paranthropus   boisei*
(Robinson, 1960); *Australopithecus* (*Zinjanthropus*) *boisei*
(Leakey, Tobias and Napier, 1964)
'Nutcracker man'

Site   Site F.L.K. I (Leakey), Bed I Olduvai Gorge, Tanzania, East
Africa. 110 miles south-west of Nairobi.

119

Found by Mrs M. D. Leakey, 17th July, 1959.

Geology Situated on the Serengeti Plain about 30 miles north of Lake Eyasi, Olduvai Gorge is a deep canyon cut through the Pleistocene and Recent deposits of East Africa. The fossiliferous strata, which rest on a lava base, are bedded and consist of a series of volcanic tuffs and lacustrine, fluviatile and wind-blown deposits which have been numbered Beds I–V from below upwards.

The skull was found approximately 22 feet from the top of Bed I, and was in process of being eroded to the surface of the slope of the gorge. The bulk of the specimen was embedded on a living floor resting on the surface of a bentonitic clay which had formed the margin of a Pleistocene lake. The geology of the Gorge has been described in detail (Leakey 1965).

Associated finds The skull was associated with stone artefacts of the Oldowan culture. There were also numerous fossilized broken bones of small amphibia, reptiles, rodents and fish.

The fossil mammalian fauna recovered from Bed I (1951–1961) is extensive and has been provisionally described. It includes several proboscideans (*Deinotherium bozasi* throughout; *Elephas cf. africanavus* at lower levels; and primitive *Elephas recki* at upper levels), several archaic pigs (including *Ectopotamochoerus sp.*, *Promesochoerus sp.*, *Notochoerus sp.*, *Potamochoerus sp.* and *Tapinochoerus sp.*), several bovids and giraffids, and many other forms such as perissodactyls, rodents, carnivores and primates (Leakey, 1965).

Dating Bed I is distinguished from Bed II by a flagstone layer chosen by Reck and Leakey in 1931 as a matter of convenience. For many years it appeared that this arbitrary line coincided with a major faunal change; it is now clear that geologically, culturally and faunally Lower Bed II belongs with Bed I. The faunal evidence has shown that Bed I and Lower Bed II must be regarded as representing the upper half of the Villafranchian (Leakey, 1965).

Potassium-argon dating of a layer near the base of Bed I has been given as 1·7 million years B.P. (Leakey, Evernden and Curtis, 1961). This age was disputed by subsequent workers (von Koenigswald, Gentner and Lippolt, 1961) who used the same method on specimens believed to come from the basalt

underlying Bed I; in their view the underlying bed is dated at
1·3 million years B.P. Until the dating of Bed I is clarified by
new estimations or new techniques it seems that the chronometric age of '*Zinjanthropus*' is about 1,500,000 years B.P.

Morphology The skull is almost complete and only lacks the mandible. It is
probably male and belonged to a young adult whose third
molars had erupted, but had not come into wear; the sutures
of the skull are still open. The specimen has not been fully
described as yet, but from the preliminary report it appears

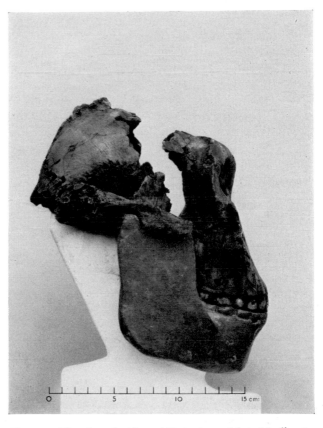

Fig. 41   The *Australopithecus* (*Zinjanthropus*) *boisei* skull artic-
ulated with a modified Natron mandible
Lateral view
*Courtesy of Dr L. S. B. Leakey and Bob Campbell
Armand Denis Productions*

121

that the cranial vault is low and the brow ridges strongly marked; the facial skeleton and palate are large and the teeth very robust. The size of the teeth led to the colloquial name, 'Nutcracker man'. A particularly striking feature of the skull is the great development around the cranium of muscular ridges such as the sagittal, occipital and supra-mastoid crests which were probably associated with a heavy mandible and powerful muscles of mastication. The mastoid processes are large and laterally prominent.

THE TEETH

The complete upper dentition is present and resembles that of the Transvaal australopithecines in some respects. The canines are small but the molars are large and rectangular, the unworn third molar showing secondary enamel wrinkling.

THE TIBIA AND FIBULA

Early in 1960, on the same living floor as the skull, a tibia and fibula were found by Dr L. S. B. Leakey and his assistants (Leakey, 1960). The upper ends of both bones are missing, but the lower articular surfaces are intact, allowing them to be fitted together. In a preliminary assessment, the bones are described as being relatively straight and well adapted to a bipedal gait at the ankle, but less well adapted at the knee. It was concluded that whilst this form was an habitual bipedal walker, the gait may well have differed considerably from that of modern man (Davis, 1964). It seems likely that these bones should not be attributed to 'Zinjanthropus' (see page 124).

Approximate   THE SKULL
Dimensions   *Leakey* (1959)
Length (Inion to glabella) 174
Breadth (At supra-mastoid crest) 138
Height (Basion to a point vertically above it in the midline) 98
Cranial Capacity 530 cc (Tobias, 1963)
Length of Palate (From the front of the incisors to a line joining the backs of third molars) 84
Width of Palate (At the second molar) 82

POST-CRANIAL BONES
Davis (1964)

	Length	*Reconstructed length*
Tibia	223	277 ($\pm$ 10)
Fibula	236	—

THE TEETH

	Upper Teeth (Crown Dimensions)							
	I1	I2	C	PM1	PM2	M1	M2	M3
Length	8·0*	7·0	9·0	11·5	12·0	15·5	17·0	16·0
Breadth	10·0*	7·0	9·5	17·0	18·0	18·0	21·0	21·0

*Damaged

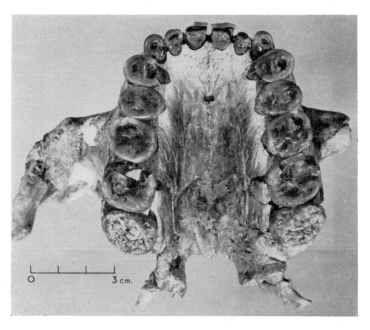

Fig. 42 The palate and dentition of *Australopithecus* (*Zinjanthropus*) *boisei*
Courtesy of Dr L. S. B. Leakey, *photographed by* R. Klomfass

Affinities In the original description it was stated that, whilst the new skull belonged patently to the sub-family *Australopithecinae*, it differed from both *Australopithecus* and *Paranthropus* 'much more than these two genera differ from each other' (Leakey, 1959). On these grounds the new genus *Zinjanthropus* was created; the trivial name *boisei* was given after a benefactor. Robinson (1960) believed that the cranial and dental characters of this skull are typically those of *Paranthropus* and proposed   123

Zinjanthropus be included in this genus (*Paranthropus boisei*). Following the discovery of further hominid remains in Bed I (*Homo habilis*), Leakey, Tobias and Napier (1964) recognized the genus *Australopithecus* as having three sub-genera within the family *Hominidae*, i.e. *Australopithecus, Paranthropus* and *Zinjanthropus*. Thus '*Zinjanthropus*' has been accepted as an East African australopithecine, sub-generically distinct from the South African forms.

Since some other examples of fossil hominids attributed to a new and perhaps more advanced form (*Homo habilis*) have been found on the same living floor some doubt has been cast upon the ownership of the tibia and fibula and indeed upon authorship of the stone tools found on this floor. It could well be that the leg bones and the tools belong to *Homo habilis*, and that *Australopithecus* (*Zinjanthropus*) *boisei* represents an intruder upon the site.

Original Property of the Government of Tanzania, East Africa; housed in the National Museum, Dar-es-Salaam.

Casts Not available at present.

References LEAKEY, L. S. B. 1959
A new fossil skull from Olduvai. *Nature 184*, 491-493.
LEAKEY, L. S. B. 1960
Recent discoveries at Olduvai Gorge. *Nature 188*, 1050-1052.
ROBINSON, J. T. 1960
The affinities of the new Olduvai australopithecine. *Nature 186*, 456-458.
LEAKEY, L. S. B., EVERNDEN J. F., and CURTIS, G. H. 1961
Age of Bed I, Olduvai Gorge, Tanganyika. *Nature 191*, 478-479.
KOENIGSWALD, G. H. R. VON, GENTNER, W., and LIPPOLT, H. J. 1961
Age of the basalt flow at Olduvai, East Africa. *Nature 192*, 720-721.
TOBIAS, P. V. 1963
Cranial capacity of *Zinjanthropus* and other australopithecines. *Nature 197*, 743-746
DAVIS, P. R. 1964
Hominid fossils from Bed I, Olduvai Gorge, Tanganyika. A tibia and fibula. *Nature 201*, 967-968.
LEAKEY, L. S. B., TOBIAS, P. V., and NAPIER, J. R. 1964
A new species of the genus *Homo* from Olduvai Gorge. *Nature 202*, 7-9.
LEAKEY, L. S. B. 1965
Olduvai Gorge 1951-61. Cambridge: Cambridge University Press.

The 'Pre-Zinjanthropus' Remains from Bed I

Synonyms and other names	*Homo habilis* (Leakey, Tobias and Napier, 1964) Pre-Zinjanthropus; Co-Zinjanthropus
Site	Site F.L.K.N.N. I (Leakey), Bed I, Olduvai Gorge, Tanzania, East Africa. 110 miles south-west of Nairobi.
Found by	Dr L. S. B. Leakey, Mrs M. D. Leakey (Foot bones, 1960); Jonathan Leakey (Mandible, 2nd November, 1960).
Geology	The remains were found in Bed I, stratigraphically about two feet below the level at which the '*Zinjanthropus*' skull and the tibia and fibula were found, but sited 300 yards away from the '*Zinjanthropus*' floor.
Associated finds	Associated with the remains were the bones of numerous tortoises, catfish and aquatic birds; also the jaw of a sabre-toothed tiger. The stone implements that were found belong to the Oldowan culture and are similar to those found on the '*Zinjanthropus*' floor. In addition a utilized bone was found and described as a lissoir.
Dating	The dating of Bed I has been discussed in relation with the '*Zinjanthropus*' skull (*q.v.*). Geologically the age difference between the sites F.L.K. I and F.L.K.N.N. I is regarded as being negligible, thus this group of specimens is believed to be of Upper Villafranchian age.
Morphology	The remains consist of two groups of hominid fossil bones belonging to at least two individuals, one adult and the other juvenile. The juvenile remains comprise parts of a pair of parietal bones, part of an occipital bone and other skull fragments, a mandible, an upper molar and parts of the skeleton of a hand; the adult bones include a clavicle, some hand bones and an almost complete left foot. THE SKULL (Olduvai Hominid 7) The two immature parietal bones are thin and incomplete, and have no sign of a sagittal crest or marked temporal lines. Restoration was facilitated by the fortunate preservation of the entire coronal and temporal borders of the left bone, and the entire occipital border of the right bone. Moreover, the anterior part of the sagittal border of the left parietal bone and

Fig. 43   The Olduvai Hominid 7 parietal bones
Type specimen of *Homo habilis*
Courtesy of Dr L. S. B. Leakey, photographed by A. R. Hughes

Fig. 44   The Olduvai Hominid 7 biparietal calvarial arch
Type specimen of *Homo habilis*
Reconstructed by Professor Tobias and A. R. Hughes
Courtesy of Dr L. S. B. Leakey and Professor P. V. Tobias, photographed by A. R. Hughes

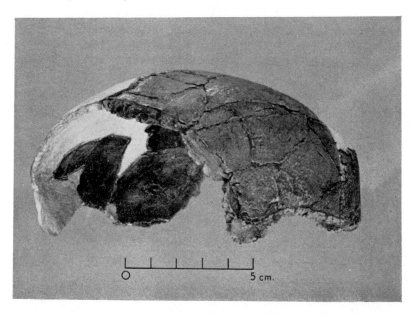

the posterior part of this border of the right parietal bone were preserved (Tobias, 1964). Thus, although the bones have no point of contact, reconstruction of the vault could proceed with confidence. Subsequently the volume of the partial endocast was estimated by water displacement.

THE MANDIBLE (Olduvai Hominid 7)

So far the mandible has not been fully described, but from the preliminary descriptions (Leakey, 1961a and b) and from examination of a cast it is apparent that it belonged to an immature individual. The jaw was broken prior to fossilization and the right side of the body has been displaced medially.

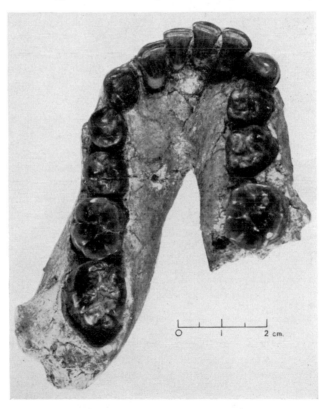

2 cm.

Fig. 45   The Olduvai Hominid 7 mandible
Type specimen of *Homo habilis*
Courtesy of Dr L. S. B. Leakey, photographed by A. R. Hughes

127

The body is very stout but its depth cannot be determined since the lower border and part of the symphysial region are missing. Both rami and their coronoid and condyloid processes are also absent.

THE TEETH

All of the permanent teeth are present in the mandible with the exception of the right second molar and both third molars. Sufficient bone is present distal to the left second molar to establish that the third molar tooth is unerupted. On the basis of present-day tooth eruption, and since the second molar is in occlusal position but is little worn, the age on death has been estimated at about twelve years (Leakey, 1961b).

The incisors are hominid in their general structure, but at least one of the premolars is elongated in that the mesiodistal length of its crown is greater than its buccolingual width.

The second molar crown is larger than the first on the left side and the molar cusp pattern is basically dryopithecine.

THE ISOLATED TOOTH

This tooth is an upper molar, probably an unerupted third molar since the roots of the tooth have not yet formed. It seems likely that it belongs with the mandible described above. Again the crown dimensions disclose mesiodistal elongation.

THE CLAVICLE

The clavicle, as yet only provisionally described, is said to have clear overall similarities to that of *Homo sapiens sapiens* (Leakey, Tobias and Napier, 1964). From the published photograph and from examination of the original it appears to have few, if any, features which distinguish it from the corresponding bone in modern man.

THE HAND BONES

Fifteen hand bones pertaining to at least two individuals, an adult and a juvenile, have been identified and described. They include proximal, intermediate and distal phalanges as well as a trapezium, a scaphoid and a capitate. The bones of the fingers are small, robust and strongly curved. The terminal phalanx of

Fig. 46   The Olduvai hand (*Homo habilis*)
            Photographed by courtesy of Dr L. S. B. Leakey
Fig. 47   The Olduvai clavicle (*Homo habilis*)
            Superior view
            Photographed by courtesy of Dr L. S. B. Leakey

Fig. 46

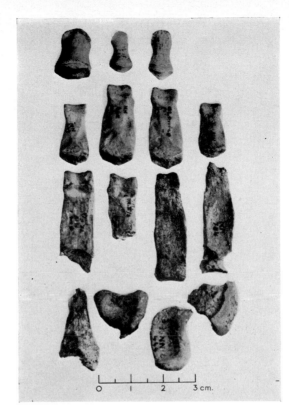

Fig. 47

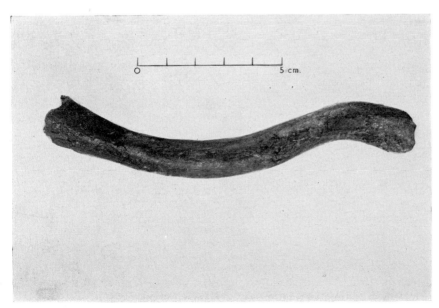

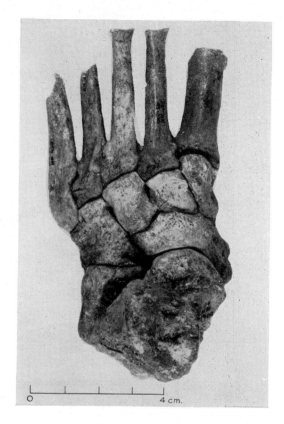

Fig. 48   The Olduvai foot (*Homo habilis*)
            Photographed by courtesy of Dr L. S. B.
            Leakey

Fig. 49   The Olduvai tibia and fibula
            Anterior view
            Photographed by courtesy of Dr L. S. B.
            Leakey

the thumb is of particular interest in that it is stout and broad, and has an impression for the insertion of flexor pollicis longus muscle. The carpal bones are damaged, but the trapezium has a well defined saddle surface.

Morphologically the hand bones cannot be closely matched by those of any known hominoid species; however, they bear a greater resemblance to juvenile modern gorilla and adult

130

Fig. 49

modern man than to those of any adult modern ape (Napier, 1962).

THE FOOT BONES (Olduvai Hominid 8)

The bones of the foot include all the left tarsal and metatarsal bones of an adult individual; all the phalanges are missing. It is clear from a preliminary examination that the principal affinities of this foot, despite its small size, are with *Homo sapiens*. The metatarsals are robust and the distribution of this robusticity in the fore-foot resembles that of modern man. The presence of an articular facet between the bases of the first and second metatarsals demonstrates unequivocally the absence of hallucial divergence which characterizes non-human primate feet. The distal row of tarsal bones form a well marked transverse arch; the ligamentous and muscular impressions upon the bones provide evidence for the static and dynamic support of the arches of the foot.

Consideration of this foot as a functional complex shows clearly that it has most of the specializations associated with the plantigrade propulsive feet of modern man (Day and Napier, 1964).

Dimensions SKULL

Estimated Cranial Capacity 673·5–680·8 cc (Central values)

Range of Estimates 642·7–723·6 cc (Tobias, 1964)

MANDIBLE

Not available.

TEETH

Tobias and von Koenigswald (1964)

			Lower Teeth (Crown Dimensions)					
		I_1	I_2	C	PM_1	PM_2	M_1	M_2	M_3
Left	l	★	★	★	9·6	10·3	14·3	15·6	—
side	b	★	★	★	10·3	10·7	12·2	13·5	—
Right	l	★	★	★	9·9	11·1	14·3	—	—
side	b	★	★	★	10·1	10·7	12·4	—	—

★ Unpublished

Third upper molar Length 13·5   Breadth 12·75 (Leakey, 1961b)

POST-CRANIAL BONES

Not available at present.

Affinities Following the discovery and preliminary description of this material it has been considered that this form is not an australopithecine and that sufficient evidence is available on which to create a new species of the genus *Homo* provided that the diagnosis of this genus is revised. This revision and a definition of the new species, *Homo habilis*, has been given by Leakey, Tobias and Napier (1964). The type specimen (the juvenile mandible and dentition, the associated upper molar and the juvenile hand bones) has been provisionally described (Leakey, 1961a and b; Napier, 1962; Tobias, 1964); further description of the material is in preparation. The type specimen is catalogued as Olduvai Hominid 7 (F.L.K.N.N. 1).

The remaining material described in this section has been regarded as representing a paratype and designated Olduvai Hominid 8 (F.L.K.N.N. 1).

Since the discovery of the material described above, further specimens have come to light at Olduvai; some of these have been regarded as representing further paratypes of *Homo habilis* whilst the remainder have been classed as referred material. (Leakey and Leakey, 1964; Leakey, Tobias and Napier, 1964). These specimens will be described in subsequent sections.

Originals Property of the Government of Tanzania, East Africa; to be housed in the National Museum, Dar-es-Salaam; at present being studied elsewhere.

Casts Not available at present.

References LEAKEY, L. S. B. 1960
Recent discoveries at Olduvai Gorge. *Nature 188*, 1050-1052.
LEAKEY, L. S. B. 1961a
New finds at Olduvai Gorge. *Nature 189*, 649-650.
LEAKEY, L. S. B. 1961b
The juvenile mandible from Olduvai. *Nature 191*, 417-418.
NAPIER, J. R. 1962
Fossil hand bones from Olduvai Gorge. *Nature 196*, 409-411.
DAY, M. H., and NAPIER, J. R. 1964
Hominid fossils from Bed I, Olduvai Gorge, Tanganyika. Fossil foot bones. *Nature 201*, 967-970.
LEAKEY, L. S. B., and LEAKEY, M. D. 1964
Recent discoveries of fossil hominids in Tanganyika; at Olduvai and near Lake Natron. *Nature 202*, 5-7.
LEAKEY, L. S. B., TOBIAS, P. V., and NAPIER, J. R. 1964
A new species of the genus *Homo* from Olduvai Gorge. *Nature 202*, 7-9.

TOBIAS, P. V. 1964
The Olduvai Bed I hominine with special reference to its cranial capacity. *Nature 202*, 3-4.
TOBIAS, P. V., and KOENIGSWALD, G. H. R. VON 1964
Comparison between the Olduvai hominines and those of Java and some implications for hominid phylogeny. *Nature 204*, 515-518.
LEAKEY, L. S. B. 1965
Olduvai Gorge 1951-61. Cambridge: Cambridge University Press.

Further Hominid Remains from Bed I

Synonyms and other names
Homo habilis (Leakey, Tobias and Napier, 1964)
Pre-Zinjanthropus; Co-Zinjanthropus

Sites
F.L.K. I and M.K. I (Leakey), Bed I, Olduvai Gorge, Tanzania, East Africa. 110 miles south-west of Nairobi.

Found by
Dr L. S. B. Leakey and his assistants.

Geology
F.L.K. I—the same site and level at which the '*Zinjanthropus*' remains were found (*q.v.*).
M.K. I—Very low in Bed I, stratigraphically the oldest remains recovered at Olduvai.

Associated finds
Oldowan stone tools. At site D.K I, geologically contemporaneous with but one mile distant from M.K. I, a rough semi-circle of loosely piled stones was found on the living floor. This has been interpreted as a rough shelter or windbreak.

Dating
Upper Villafranchian. Refer to the dating of the '*Zinjanthropus*' skull (page 120).

Morphology
F.L.K. I OLDUVAI HOMINID 6
The remains consist of a left lower first premolar; an unworn upper molar (M1 or M2) which has partly developed roots and an almost complete crown; and some fragments of the cranial vault. The teeth are small, particularly in their buccolingual breadth, giving them an elongated appearance and a Length/Breadth Index outside the known range for australopithecine teeth or those of Peking man (*Homo erectus pekinensis*)
M.K. I OLDUVAI HOMINID 4
A fragment of the left side of the body of a mandible containing a fully erupted molar (M2 or M3). The tooth is small and narrow by comparison with australopithecine teeth, but large by comparison with *Homo erectus* molars. There are several other isolated tooth fragments.

Dimensions
F.L.K. I Not available at present.
M.K. I Mandibular width, level with molar tooth *in situ*—
19·2   Molar Length 15·1   Molar Breadth 13·0

Affinities
Provisionally these specimens have been described as paratypes   135

Further Hominid Remains

of *Homo habilis* on account of their general similarities to the type specimen of this species recovered from Bed I.

Originals   Property of the Government of Tanzania, to be housed in the National Museum, Dar-es-Salaam; at present being studied elsewhere.

Casts   Not available at present.

References   LEAKEY, L. S. B., TOBIAS, P. V., and NAPIER, J. R. 1964
A new species of the genus *Homo* from Olduvai Gorge. *Nature 202* 7–9.
LEAKEY, L. S. B. 1965
Olduvai Gorge 1951–61. Cambridge: Cambridge University Press.

The Bed II Calvarium

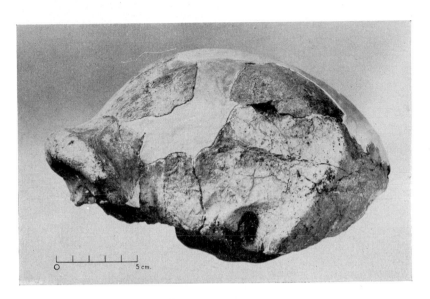

Fig. 50   The Olduvai Hominid 9 calvarium
Formerly called 'Chellean man'
Reconstructed by Professor P. V. Tobias and A. R. Hughes
*Courtesy of Dr L. S. B. Leakey and Professor P. V. Tobias, photographed by
A. R. Hughes*

Synonyms   'Chellean Man', Olduvai Hominid 9
and other names

Site   Site L.L.K. (Leakey) Bed II, Olduvai Gorge, Tanzania, East
Africa, 110 miles south-west of Nairobi.

Found by   Dr L. S. B. Leakey, 2nd December, 1960.

Geology   Situated on the Serengeti Plain about 30 miles north of Lake
Eyasi, Olduvai Gorge is a deep canyon cut through the Pleistocene and Recent deposits of East Africa. The strata, which rest
on a lava base, are bedded and consist of a series of volcanic
tuffs and lacustrine, fluviatile and wind-blown deposits which
have been numbered Beds I–V from below upwards. The
skull was found 15–20 feet below the top of Bed II in land laid
tuffs deposited near the margin of a lake (Hay, 1963).

Associated finds   At the same geological level, but some 100 yards away, were   137

found numerous hand-axes said to represent Stage III of the Chellean culture, and the bones of large animals. There is some evidence that these bones have been broken for the extraction of marrow.

The fossil mammalian fauna found in Bed II is extensive and falls into two principal groups (Upper Bed II and Lower Bed II), thus a faunal break occurs within Bed II.

Lower Bed II contains several forms known from Bed I (e.g. *Deinotherium bozasi*, primitive *Elephas recki*) whilst Upper Bed II contains many giant herbivores including hippopotamus (*Hippopotamus gorgops*), pigs (*Afrochoerus nicoli, Mesochoerus olduvaiensis, Potamochoerus majus*), giant sheep (*Pelorovis oldowayensis*), equids (*Equus oldowayensis, Stylohipparion albertense*); also large carnivores, rhinoceroses and primates (Leakey, 1965).

Dating The discovery of a faunal, climatic and cultural break within Bed II has led to a revision of the dating of this layer. It seems that Lower Bed II is best regarded as belonging to the closing stages of the Upper Villafranchian whilst Upper Bed II is of Middle Pleistocene age. The Chellean skull was found in Upper Bed II.

Potassium-argon dating of Bed II material has suggested a chronological age of 490,000 years B.P. (Evernden and Curtis, 1963); however, this determination has been disputed.

Morphology The find consists of the greater part of a thick calvarium which lacks face, base and part of the vault. The frontal region is flattened, the nuchal crest prominent and the mastoid processes small. The brow ridges are large and flaring. Up to the present the specimen is only provisionally described.

Dimensions Length 209   Breadth 150 (Leakey)
Cranial Index *c.* 72

Affinities Assessment of this find must remain provisional until the specimen is fully described, but preliminary opinions suggest that it shares several features with the pithecanthropines (*Homo erectus*) of the Far East. On the other hand the Olduvai Bed II calvarium is said to show a certain resemblance to the Steinheim skull and to the skulls from Broken Hill and Saldanha (Leakey), in particular the outline of the calvarium as seen from above.

The Bed II Calvarium

Original Property of the Government of Tanzania; to be housed in the National Museum, Dar-es-Salaam; at present being studied elsewhere.

Casts Not available at present.

References LEAKEY, L. S. B. 1961
New finds at Olduvai Gorge. *Nature 189*, 649-650.
NAPIER, J. R., and WEINER, J. S. 1962
Olduvai Gorge and human origins. *Antiquity 36*, 41-47.
HAY, R. L. 1963
Stratigraphy of Bed I through IV, Olduvai Gorge, Tanganyika. *Science 139*, 829-833.
EVERNDEN, J. F., and CURTIS, G. H. 1963
In Hay, R. L. (1963) *Ibid. 139*, 829-833.
LEAKEY, L. S. B. 1965
Olduvai Gorge 1951-61. Cambridge: Cambridge University Press.

Further Hominid Remains from Bed II

Synonyms and other names   Homo habilis (Leakey, Tobias and Napier, 1964)

Site   Sites M.N.K. II and F.L.K. II (Leakey), Bed II, Olduvai Gorge, Tanzania, East Africa. 110 miles south-west of Nairobi.

Found by   Dr L. S. B. Leakey, Mrs M. D. Leakey and their assistants, October, 1963.

Geology   M.N.K. II
This site is a living floor placed midway in Bed II, but the deposits appear to antedate the advent of hand-axes.
F.L.K. II (*Maiko Gully*)
The specimens recovered from this site were surface finds that had been eroded out and then trampled by cattle. It is considered that they are derived from deposits 3–4 feet above the marker bed at the top of Bed I, and thus very low in Bed II.

Associated finds   It is not known at present whether there were any stone tools or fossil mammalian bones directly associated with the hominid remains from this site.

Dating   Probably Lower Middle Pleistocene.

Morphology   M.N.K. II OLDUVAI HOMINID 13
This individual is represented by the vault of a small skull, the greater part of a mandible and parts of both maxillae. The vault consists of most of the occipital bone which articulates at the lambda with both parietals, part of the frontal and parts of both temporal bones each bearing a mandibular fossa and foramen ovale. The teeth are elongated mesiodistally and narrowed labiolingually.
The distal half of a humeral shaft, excluding its extremity, may belong to this individual.
M.N.K. II OLDUVAI HOMINID 14
A broken juvenile skull represented by part of the right parietal bone, two smaller vault fragments, and parts of both temporal bones including the mandibular fossa.
M.N.K. II OLDUVAI HOMINID 15
Three adult teeth were recovered from this site, midway in Bed II.

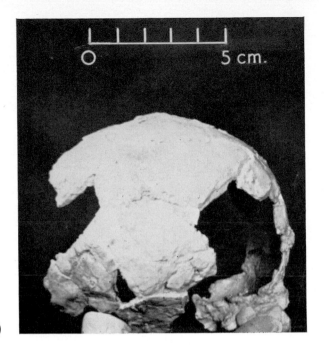

Fig. 51 (a)

Fig. 51 (a) The Olduvai Hominid 13 skull
bones
Occipital view
Courtesy of Dr L. S. B. Leakey
(b) The Olduvai Hominid 13 man-
dible from Lower Bed II
Occlusal view
Courtesy of Dr L. S. B. Leakey

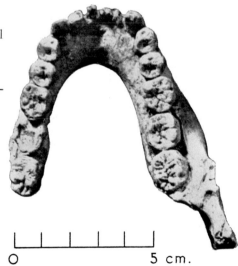

Fig. 51 (b)

F.L.K. II OLDUVAI HOMINID 16

A fragmentary skull with part of the upper and lower dentition was recovered from Maiko Gully. The skull fragments include parts of the frontal bone with both outer orbital margins and supra-orbital regions, several fragments of the parietals, and part of the occipital bone. The region of the glabella is missing.

Dimensions The only measurements available are the crown dimensions of the teeth of Hominid 13.

Tobias and von Koenigswald (1964)

Olduvai Hominid 13 Upper and Lower Teeth (Crown Dimensions)

		PM1	PM2	M1	M2	M3
Upper	l	8·3	8·7	12·5	12·8	12·0
Teeth	b	11·4	11·5	12·6	13·8	13·1
Lower	l	—	8·9	12·7	13·8	14·6
Teeth	b	—	9·8	11·6	12·2	12·5

Affinities ### M.N.K. II OLDUVAI HOMINID 13

This has been attributed to *Homo habilis* and designated a paratype specimen of this species. The teeth are said to be small by comparison with those of the *Australopithecinae* but their dimensions probably fall within the range of variation of those of the fossil *Homininae*.

The Occipital/Sagittal Index for this specimen is believed to lie outside the known range for australopithecines and for *Homo erectus pekinensis* but within the range of *Homo sapiens*.

M.N.K. II OLDUVAI HOMINID 14

This material is referred until further studies are completed.

M.N.K. II OLDUVAI HOMINID 15

This material is referred until further studies are completed. However, Tobias has suggested that these teeth are 'within the range' of australopithecine teeth and should not be included with *Homo habilis* (Tobias and von Koenigswald, 1964).

F.L.K. II OLDUVAI HOMINID 16

This material is referred until further studies are completed. However, Tobias has suggested that the teeth are 'within the range' of australopithecine teeth and should not be included with *Homo habilis* (Tobias and von Koenigswald, 1964).

Originals Property of the Government of Tanzania; to be housed in the National Museum, Dar-es-Salaam; at present being studied elsewhere.

Casts Not available at present.

References LEAKEY, L. S. B., and LEAKEY, M. D. 1964
Recent discoveries of fossil hominids in Tanganyika; at Olduvai and near Lake Natron. *Nature 202,* 5-7.
LEAKEY, L. S. B., TOBIAS, P. V., and NAPIER, J. R. 1964
A new species of the genus *Homo* from Olduvai Gorge. *Nature 202,* 7-9.
TOBIAS, P. V., and KOENIGSWALD, G. H. R. VON 1964
Comparison between the Olduvai homines and those of Java and some implications for hominid phylogeny. *Nature 204,* 515-518
LEAKEY, L. S. B. 1965
Olduvai Gorge 1951-61. Cambridge: Cambridge University Press.

The Natron Mandible

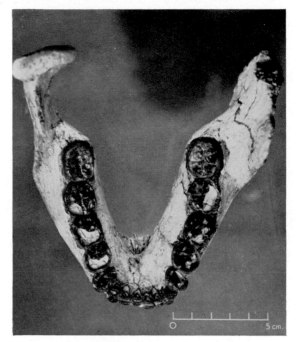

Fig. 52 The mandible from Lake Natron, Tanzania
*Courtesy of Dr L. S. B. Leakey, photographed by
L. P. Morley*

During January, 1964 at Peninj, west of Lake Natron, East
Africa, a large and almost perfect mandible containing the
complete adult lower dentition was recovered by Mr Kamoya
Kimeu working under the supervision of Richard Leakey.
The deposits from which it was obtained are believed to be
equivalent to the Bed II deposits at Olduvai Gorge, some 50
miles away. The mandible has been described as unmistak-
ably australopithecine and from published photographs seems
to resemble the Swartkrans jaw (SK 23). No further information is available at the present regarding the morphology
or dimensions of the new specimen.

Reference   LEAKEY, L. S. B., and LEAKEY, M. D. 1964
Recent discoveries of fossil hominids in Tanganyika: at Olduvai and
near Lake Natron. *Nature 202*, 5-7.

The Kanam Mandible

Fig. 53   The Kanam mandible
Anterior view
Courtesy of the Trustees of the British Museum (Nat. Hist.)

Synonyms and other names	*Homo kanamensis* (Leakey, 1935) Kanam man
Site	Near Kendu on the shore of the south side of Kavirondo Gulf, Lake Victoria, near the foot of Homa Mountain, Kenya, East Africa.
Found by	An assistant of Dr L. S. B. Leakey, 29th March, 1932.
Geology	The mandible was recovered from a deposit which had formed the bed of a Pleistocene lake. The precise location of the find is not known with certainty as subsequent erosion has altered the terrain.
Associated finds	With the mandible were some doubtful stone tools and a mammalian fossil fauna. The forms recognized include a proboscidean (*Deinotherium sp.*), hippopotamus (*Hippopotamus imaguncula*) and a mammoth (*Mammuthus (Archidiskodon) planifrons*).

L̥FM

145

The Kanam Mandible

Dating   The dating of this find has been given as Lower Pleistocene on geological, faunal and archaeological grounds (Leakey, 1933, 1935).

Unfortunately this date has been the subject of controversy, partly because of the uncertain stratigraphy and doubtful geological age (Boswell, 1935) but also because comparative fluorine and uranium tests have given ambivalent results (Oakley, 1952, 1958, 1960). However, the associated fauna is perhaps Lower Villafranchian and indicates strongly that the deposit is of Lower Pleistocene age; it remains to be shown that the jaw is contemporaneous with the deposit in which it was said to be found.

Morphology   The fossil consists of part of the body of a mandible which extends from the distal root of the right first molar, to the vicinity of the left second premolar. Only the right premolars are in place, and both are damaged and worn; the incisor sockets are small but the canine socket is larger. The lower border of the body of the mandible is broken away and the posterior region of the chin is distorted by a pathological out-growth of bone (Lawrence, 1935) giving the appearance of a well developed chin. The specimen was re-examined by Tobias (1960) who showed that there was evidence of

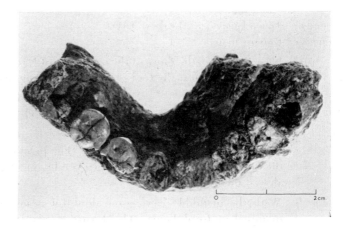

Fig 54 The Kanam mandible
Occlusal view
Courtesy of the Trustees of the British Museum (Nat. Hist.)   146

compensatory bone development in the region of the chin, and noted a genial fossa and a transverse mandibular torus amongst other archaic features.

Dimensions Tobias (1960)
Symphysial depth 40·5
Body depth at M1 40·0
Body thickness at M1 16·5

Affinities Originally Keith thought, with Leakey, that the Kanam mandible was evidence of the early development of a modern type of man, but neither knew of the dental characters of the australopithecines at this time. Later Keith said that the small front teeth of the Kanam jaw suggested a closer relationship to the australopithecines than to modern man (Keith, 1948). This possibility could not be excluded by Tobias (1960) neither could its possible affinity with *Atlanthropus*, but the balance of evidence led him to suggest that the Kanam jaw may represent a third African group showing features inter-mediate between *Atlanthropus* and modern man exemplified by Rabat and Dire Dawa. Whether such a group can be termed 'Neanderthaloid' with the European affinities that this term implies is a matter for further analysis. After fully reviewing the position Tobias (1962) stated that, in any event, the jaw is neither sapient nor modern, nor is it pre-sapient in the sense used by Vallois (1958).

It is possible that the status of this find may have to be reviewed in the light of the new material (*Homo habilis*) which has been found in East Africa.

Original British Museum (Natural History), Cromwell Road, South Kensington, London, S.W.7.

Casts The University Museum, University of Pennsylvania, Phila-delphia 4, Pennsylvania, U.S.A.

References LEAKEY, L. S. B. 1933
The status of the Kanam mandible and the Kanjera skulls. (Report of a conference at Cambridge.) *Man 33*, 200-201.
LEAKEY, L. S. B. 1935
Stone age races of Kenya. London: Oxford University Press.
LAWRENCE, J. W. P. 1935
In *Stone age races of Kenya* (Appendix A), L. S. B. Leakey. London: Oxford University Press.

BOSWELL, P. G. H. 1935
Human remains from Kanam and Kanjera, Kenya Colony. *Nature* *135*, 371.

LEAKEY, L. S. B. 1936
Fossil human remains from Kanam and Kanjera, Kenya Colony. *Nature 138*, 643.

KEITH, A. 1948
A new theory of human evolution. London: Watts.

OAKLEY, K. P. 1953
Dating fossil human remains. In *Anthropology today.* Ed. A. L. Kroeber, pp. 43-56. Chicago: Chicago University Press.

OAKLEY, K. P. 1958
Physical anthropology in the British Museum. In *The scope of physical anthropology and its place in academic studies.* Eds. D. F. Roberts and J. S. Weiner. London: The Wenner-Gren Foundation for Anthropological Research, pp. 51-54.

VALLOIS, H. V. 1958
La grotte de Fontéchevade II. *Archs Inst. Paléont. hum.* Mem. *29*, 1-262.

OAKLEY, K. P. 1960
The Kanam jaw. *Nature 185*, 945-946.

TOBIAS, P. V. 1960
The Kanam jaw. *Nature 185*, 946-947.

TOBIAS, P. V. 1962
A re-examination of the Kanam mandible. *Proc. Fourth Pan-African Cong. Prehist., Leopoldville 1959*, pp. 341-360. Tervuren: Musée Royal de l'Afrique Centrale.

The Chad Skull Fragments

Synonyms and other names	*Tchadanthropus uxoris* (Coppens, 1965) The Chad australopithecine
Found by	Y. Coppens, 1960.
Geology	The skull was found in a Pleistocene lake deposit consisting of 20 metres of sandstone.
Associated finds	With the skull fragment were the teeth of extinct elephant (*Loxodonta atlantica*). No artefacts were found.
Dating	The find is possibly of Late Lower or Early Middle Pleistocene age; however, this dating is provisional until more evidence is available of the age of the deposit and the contemporaneity of the specimen and its deposit is confirmed.
Morphology	The specimen consists of a broken frontal bone and some facial bones of both sides. The frontal is steep having a continuous brow ridge and little post-orbital constriction. The cranial capacity is said to be large. The face is prognathic, having large maxillae and a broad zygomatic bone; the orbits are large and the infra-orbital foramen is single. The arrangement of the alveolar bone around the incisor and canine sockets suggests that there was no diastema and that the canine was small.

Dimensions Coppens (1965)
Biorbital breadth 116

	Width	Height	Index
Right orbit	46	35	76

Affinities	It was claimed at first that this hominid skull fragment belonged to an australopithecine, probably a female *Paranthropus*, in view of the general features of the skull, the high cranial capacity, reduced post-orbital constriction, tall orbits and broad zygomatic bone. It has been suggested, however, that this cranio-facial skull fragment did not belong to a member of the sub-family *Australopithecinae* and that it is probably a northern representative of *Homo habilis* (Leakey, Tobias and Napier, 1964). Recently Coppens (1965) has revised his original view and now believes that this specimen represents a hominid whose

149

grade of evolution is intermediate between that of the australopithecines and the pithecanthropines, but lying nearer the latter; possibly equivalent to the structural grade of Tobias and von Koenigswald (1964) which contains *Telanthropus*, Bed II *Homo habilis* (M.N.K. II) and Pithecanthropus IV.

Until the specimen has been fully described and compared with other hominids any assessment of its affinities must be regarded with caution.

Original Institut de Paléontologie, Muséum national d'Histoire naturelle, 8, Rue de Buffon, Paris–5ᵉ, France.

Casts Not available at present.

References COPPENS, Y. 1961
Découverte d'un australopithéciné dans le Villafranchien du Tchad. *C. R. Acad. Sci. Paris 252*, 3851–3852.
COPPENS, Y. 1961
Un Australopithèque au Sahara (Nord-Tchad). *Bull. Soc. préhist. franç. 58*, 756–757.
COPPENS, Y. 1962
Prises de date pour le gisements paléontologiques quarternaires et archéologiques découverts au cours d'une mission de deux mois dans le nord du Tchad. *Bull. Soc. préhist. franç. 59*, 260-267.
COPPENS, Y. 1962
Deux gisements de vertebres villafranchiens du Tchad. *Proc. Fourth Pan-African Cong. Prehist., Leopoldville, 1959*, pp. 299-315. Tervuren: Musée Royal de l'Afrique Centrale.
LEAKEY, L. S. B., TOBIAS, P. V., and NAPIER, J. R. 1964
A new species of the genus *Homo* from Olduvai Gorge. *Nature 202*, 7-9.
TOBIAS, P. V., and KOENIGSWALD, G. H. R. VON, 1964
Comparison between the Olduvai homines and those of Java and some implications for hominid phylogeny. *Nature 204*, 515-518.
COPPENS, Y. 1965
L'Hominien du Tchad. *C. R. Acad. Sci. Paris 260*, 2869-2871.

Southern Africa

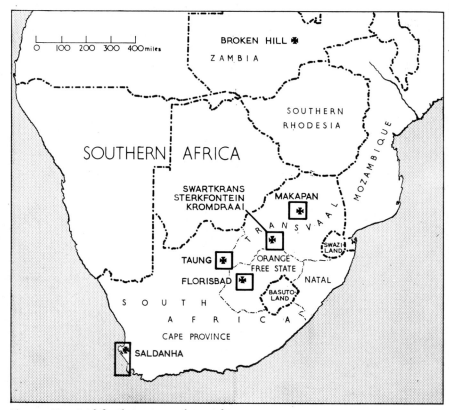

Fig. 55 Hominid fossil sites in southern Africa

Rhodesian Man

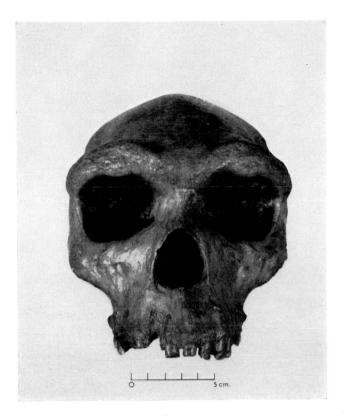

Fig. 56   The Rhodesian skull
Frontal view
*Photographed by courtesy of the Trustees of the British
Museum (Nat. Hist.)*

Synonyms   Homo rhodesiensis (Woodward, 1921); *Cyphanthropus rhod-*
and other names   esiensis (Pycraft, 1928); *Homo sapiens rhodesiensis* (Campbell,
1964)
Rhodesian man; Broken Hill man
Site   The Broken Hill Mine, Broken Hill, Zambia.
Found by   T. Zwigelaar, 17th June, 1921, cranium; other remains found
by A. S. Armstrong, 1921, and H. Hrdlička, 1925.
Geology   The mine included two kopjes or small hills of dolomitic   153

limestone which contained lead and zinc ore. One of the hills was tunnelled at its base by a cave filled with fossilized and mineralized bones. During the clearance of this cavern the skull was found at its farthest and deepest point about 60 feet below ground level. Subsequent excavations produced the rest of the remains, but continued mining has destroyed the original cave.

Associated finds   With the hominid bones, although not associated on a living floor, were some quartz and chert stone tools. These implements belong to African flake cultures known as the Stillbay and Proto-Stillbay of the Middle Stone Age. In addition there were several bolas stones and a few bone tools.

The associated fauna included fossil birds, reptiles and mammals, many of which belong to living species. A recent mammalian faunal list for the Broken Hill site has been given by Cooke (1964); forms identified include a large primate (?*Simopithecus sp.*), mongoose (*Herpestes ichneumon*), large carnivores (*Panthera leo, Panthera pardus*), an extinct carnivore (*Leptailurus hintoni*), extinct elephant (*Loxodonta africana*), zebra (*Equus burchelli*), black rhinoceros (*Diceros bicornis*) and several artiodactyls including an extinct buffalo (*Homoioceras bainii*).

Dating   Initially it was believed that the skull and the other bones may be of different ages because of variations in the mineral content of the specimens. Oakley (1947) suggested that these differences may be due to local variations in the mineral constituents of the soil at the site of burial. Further chemical and radiometric investigations indicate that the skull and the other bones are ancient and of the same age (Oakley, 1957, 1958). A new excavation at Broken Hill has produced more stone implements of a similar type to those found with the skeletal remains. The new finds have been attributed to the early Middle Stone Age (Upper Pleistocene) after comparison with the tools from another Rhodesian site which contains an established sequence (Clark, 1947, 1959). Thus on faunal, archaeological and chemical grounds it seems that Rhodesian man lived during the Upper Pleistocene.

Morphology   The remains belong to at least two individuals and consist of a skull, a parietal, a maxilla, a humerus, a sacrum, two ilia, a broken femur, the upper end of a second femur and two tibiae.   154

THE SKULL

The cranium is heavily built with massive brow ridges, a retreating forehead and a flattened vault; the occipital region is rounded above the occipital torus but flattened beneath. The foramen magnum is placed well forward and faces downward, indicating an erect head carriage. The mastoid process is of moderate size but the supra-mastoid crest is prominent. The greatest diameter of the cranium is situated very low.

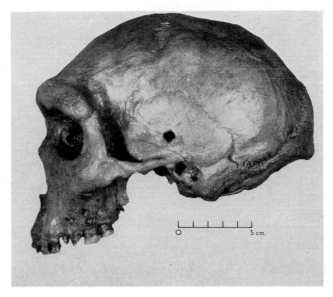

Fig. 57   The Rhodesian skull
Left lateral view
Photographed by courtesy of the Trustees of the British Museum (Nat. Hist.)

The face is very long with inflated, but flat, maxillae having no canine fossae; the lateral walls of the nose pass smoothly on to the face but there is a nasal spine at the apex of two ridges which lead back to join the lateral wall half-way up the nasal opening. The alveolar processes of the maxillae are very deep and the bony palate is extremely large both in width and length.

The separate maxilla was re-examined by Wells (1947) who   155 found that it differs in several respects from the corresponding bone in the skull. It is a smaller bone with a transversely arranged zygomatic process and a canine fossa 'modelling essentially as in modern human skulls'. However, he concluded that the maxilla and the skull belonged to a single type, perhaps not even specifically distinct from *Homo sapiens*.

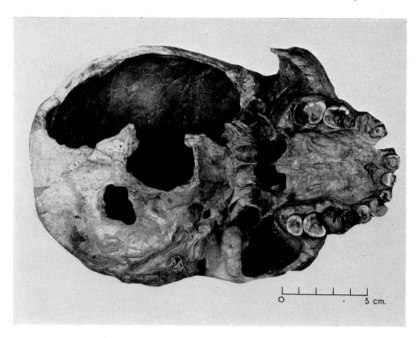

Fig. 58 The Rhodesian skull
Basal view
Photographed by courtesy of the Trustees o, the British Museum (Nat. Hist.)

THE TEETH
The teeth are large and set in a horseshoe-shaped arcade. All the teeth are considerably worn and most are affected by caries. The crowns are generally of modern form and the third molar is reduced in size.

THE POST-CRANIAL BONES
These bones have few, if any, features which lie outside the range of normal variation of modern man. The limb bones are stout and long, indicating tall stature, whilst the lower limb

156

bones have no features which are incompatible with an upright stance and a bipedal striding gait.

Dimensions   SKULL
Morant (1928)
Max. Length 208·5   Max. Breadth 144·5
Cranial Index 69·3 (Dolichocephalic)
Cranial Capacity 1,280 cc
POST-CRANIAL BONES
Pycraft (1928)
Sacrum Length 105   Sacrum Breadth 110

		Right	Left
Femora:	Max. Diameter of Heads	52·0	50·0
	Ant./Post. Diameter of Shaft	30·0	27·5
Humerus:	Ant./Post. Diameter of Shaft	20·0	—

TEETH
Pycraft (1928)

			Upper Teeth (Crown Dimensions)					
		I_1	I_2	C	PM_1	PM_2	M_1	M_2	M_3
Left	l	8·0	7·0	10·0	7·5	—	—	13·0	9·0
Side	b	8·5	8·0	11·0	11·0	—	—	14·0	12·0
Right	l	8·0	—	—	—	—	(14·0)	12·5	—
Side	b	8·5	—	—	—	—	13·5	13·5	—

( ) Estimated

Affinities   The Rhodesian cranium has several points of similarity with those of European Neanderthal man whilst remaining distinct in the structure of the post-cranial bones, a situation which raised doubts about the correctness of associating the type skull with the remainder of the skeleton. These doubts were reinforced by the rather unsatisfactory circumstances of the find. However, the chemical and radiometric evidence seems to have established the contemporaneity of the remains.

The resemblances of the Rhodesian skeletons to that of Neanderthal man did not escape Woodward (1921) but the position of the foramen magnum being much more modern in the Rhodesian cranium than in the Neanderthalers available to him, he felt obliged to create a new species of man, *Homo rhodesiensis*. Pycraft (1928) was convinced of the peculiarity of the stance and gait of this form and created a new genus,

Cyphanthropus rhodesiensis or 'Stooping man', a concept which gained little support since Le Gros Clark (1928) explained the error of interpretation which led to this viewpoint.

Morant (1928) has shown that the skull can be distinguished from those of Neanderthal man by a number of metrical characteristics and that it tends to resemble *Homo sapiens*; however, he concluded that Rhodesian man and Neanderthal man seem more closely related to each other than either is to *Homo sapiens* and also that they are equally related to all races of *Homo sapiens*.

Broken Hill man was placed near the point of divergence of Neanderthal and modern man by von Bonin (1928–1930) on the basis of further comparative skull measurements.

The discovery of the Saldanha calvarium (*q.v.*) is particularly significant at this point. In its form and dimensions it closely resembles the Rhodesian skull, confirming that this is not an isolated or aberrant specimen. Singer (1954) regarded the Rhodesian and Saldanha people as African Neanderthalians, unlike the European but similar to the Asiatic representatives of this group (Solo man).

Howell (1957) has denied Neanderthal penetration 'south of the Sahara' and regards Rhodesian man, as well as other related southern African forms, as racially distinct. Recently, in a review of the position of Rhodesian man, Wells (1957) suggests that the primitive pithecanthropine stock gave rise to a basic type of *Homo sapiens* which became widely dispersed and underwent regional differentiation into a number of offshoots represented by Broken Hill, Neanderthal and Solo man—these three lines becoming extremely specialized and then extinct.

Finally Coon (1963) seeks to show that Rhodesian and Saldanha man are both forms of *Homo erectus* leading towards a possible negro evolutionary line, as a part of his general polyphyletic theory of racial origin. This view has received little support and much criticism.

It is clear that the principal resemblances of the Rhodesian skull are to the Saldanha specimen, but the classification of these remains is still controversial. It would be widely agreed that Rhodesian man is a member of the genus *Homo* but the subgeneric group to which he belongs remains in dispute.   158

However, opinion is growing in favour of classifying Neanderthal and Neanderthaloid forms as sub-species of *Homo sapiens* (Campbell, 1964).

Originals British Museum (Natural History), Cromwell Road, South Kensington, London, S.W.7.

Casts The University Museum, University of Pennsylvania, Philadelphia 4, Pennsylvania, U.S.A.

References WOODWARD, A. S. 1921
A new cave man from Rhodesia, South Africa. *Nature 108*, 371-372.
PYCRAFT, W. P. *et al.* 1928
Rhodesia man and associated remains. Ed. F. A. Bather, London: British Museum (Natural History).
CLARK, W. E. LE GROS 1928
Rhodesian man. *Man 28*, 206-207.
MORANT, G. M. 1928
Studies of Paleolithic Man III. The Rhodesian skull and its relations to Neanderthaloid and modern types. *Ann. Eugen. 3*, 337-360.
BONIN, G. VON 1928-1930
Studien zum *Homo rhodesiensis*. *Z. Morph. anthr. 2*, 347-381.
CLARK, J. D. *et al.* 1947
New studies on Rhodesian man. *J. R. anthrop. Inst. 77*, 7-32.
WELLS, L. H. 1947
In *New studies on Rhodesian man*. J. D. Clark *et al.* II. A note on the broken maxillary fragment from the Broken Hill cave. *J. R. anthrop. Inst. 77*, 11-12.
SINGER, R. 1954
The Saldanha skull from Hopefield, South Africa. *Am. J. Phys. Anthrop. 12*, 345-362.
OAKLEY, K. P. 1957
The dating of the Broken Hill, Florisbad and Saldanha skulls. *Proc. Third Pan-African Cong. Prehist., Livingstone, 1955*. Ed. J. D. Clark. pp. 76-79. London: Chatto and Windus.
WELLS, D. H. 1957
The place of the Broken Hill skull among human types. *Ibid.*, pp. 172-174.
OAKLEY, K. P. 1958
The dating of Broken Hill (Rhodesian man). In *Hundert Jahre Neanderthaler*. Ed. G. H. R. von Koenigswald, pp. 265-266. Utrecht: Kemink en Zoon.
CLARK, J. D. 1959
Further excavations at Broken Hill, Northern Rhodesia. *J. R. anthrop. Inst. 89*, 201-231.
LEAKEY, L. S. B. 1959
A preliminary re-assessment of the fossil fauna from Broken Hill, N. Rhodesia. *J. R. anthrop. Inst. 89*, 225-231.

COON, C. S. 1963
The origin of races, pp. 621-627. London: Jonathan Cape.
CAMPBELL, B. 1964
Quantitative taxonomy and human evolution. In *Classification and human evolution*. Ed. S. L. Washburn, pp. 50-74. London: Methuen and Co. Ltd.
COOKE, H. B. S. 1964
Pleistocene mammal faunas of Africa, with particular reference to Southern Africa. In *African ecology and human evolution*. Eds. F. C. Howell and F. Bourlière, pp. 65-116. London: Methuen and Co. Ltd.

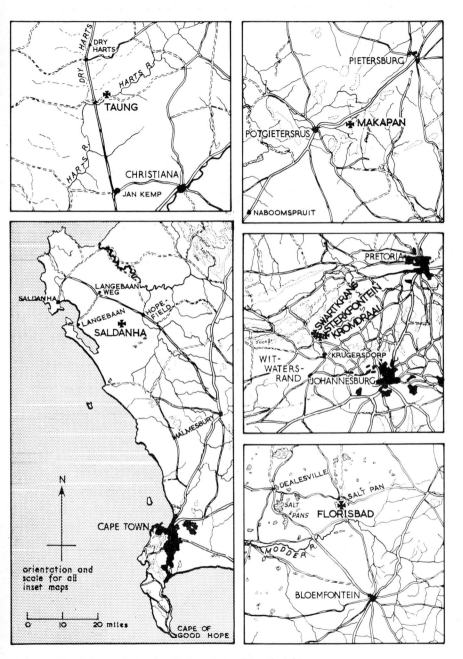

Fig. 59   Hominid fossil sites in the Republic of South Africa

MFM

The Taung Skull

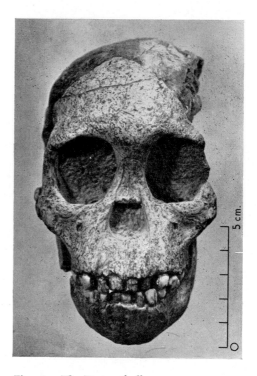

Fig. 60   The Taung skull
Frontal view
*Courtesy of Professor P. V. Tobias,
photographed by A. R. Hughes*

Synonyms
and other names

Australopithecus africanus (Dart, 1925)
Homo transvaalensis (Mayr, 1950); *Australopithecus africanus africanus* (Robinson, 1954)
'Ape-man'; 'Man-ape'; 'Near-man'

Site

A limestone quarry six miles south-west of Taung railway station, 80 miles north of Kimberley, Bechuanaland, South Africa.

Found by

A quarryman, M. de Bruyn; recognized by R. A. Dart, November, 1924.

Geology

The skull was found in sandy breccia which formed the filling   162

of a cave cut into the face of a dolomitic limestone escarpment. The Taung deposit is part of the Thasbeek Travertine
(Peabody, 1954), the oldest of four limestone masses which
form the valley of the Harts river. Mining of the tuffaceous
limestone, for the manufacture of cement, led to the discovery
after a blasting operation.

Associated finds No artefacts have been recovered from the cave deposit. The
fossil mammalian fauna found with the skull includes three
insectivores (*Elephantulus cf. brachyrhynchus, Mylomygale
spiersi, Crocidura taungensis*), a bat (*Rhinolophus cf. capensis*),
several baboons (*Parapapio antiquus, P. jonesi, P. whitei,
P. izodi, P. wellsi*), numerous rodents (*Thallomys debruyni,
Gypsorhynchus darti, G. minor, Cryptomys robertsi, Pedetes
gracile, Dendromus antiquus, Protomys campbelli, Petromus minor*),
two hyraces (*Procavia capensis, P. transvaalensis*) and two artiodactyls (*Cephalophus parvus, Oreotragus longiceps*).
The bones neither of carnivora nor proboscidea have been
positively identified in the deposit (Cooke, 1963).

Dating Accurate dating of the remains from Taung has proved
difficult since material from this type of deposit is not amen-
able to the chemical and radiometric techniques that are
available at present. However, Kurtén (1962) attributed the
Taung skull to the First Interglacial (Günz–Mindel or Antepenultimate Interglacial) on the grounds of faunal correlation.
However, the balance of evidence from geological and faunal
studies suggests that the Taung deposit was laid down early in
the sequence of australopithecine sites, during the Upper
Villafranchian part of the Lower Pleistocene (Ewer 1957;
Oakley 1954, 1957, 1964).

Morphology THE SKULL
The specimen consists of the greater part of a juvenile skull
which contains a remarkable endocast of the brain. The facial
skeleton is intact and the dentition complete. Most of the base
of the skull is preserved but much of the vault is missing. The
lower parts of the body and the angles of the mandible are
broken.
The cranium appears to be globular with neither frontal
flattening nor supra-orbital torus formation, but the glabella
is prominent; the sphenoid and parietal bones appear to have

163

been in contact in the temporal fossa. The foramen magnum is set well forward beneath the skull. The face is undistorted, having large rounded orbits, flattened nasal bones and a square nasal opening which runs without interruption on to the maxillae; there is no nasal spine. The nasal flattening gives the face a 'dished' appearance which is accentuated by the degree of sub-nasal prognathism of the maxillae.

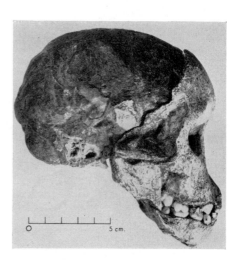

Fig. 61   The Taung skull
Right lateral view
Courtesy of Professor P. V. Tobias,
photographed by A. R. Hughes

The dental arcade is regular and parabolic enclosing a shallow palatal vault marked by an incisive foramen; the palatine foramina are set behind a line drawn posterior to the first permanent molars.

MANDIBLE

This bone is represented by the body and the alveolar processes of bone with the teeth in place. The angles of the mandible and the rami are largely absent. The symphysial region slopes backwards, there being neither chin nor simian shelf present. The body of the mandible is thickened particularly in the region of the erupting first molar.

TEETH

The milk dentition is complete in both upper and lower jaws, and the upper and lower first permanent molars are in process of eruption.

The Upper Deciduous Incisors are heavily worn and damaged.   164

The teeth are well separated one from another, a feature characteristic of other hominids at this stage of dental development.

The Upper Deciduous Canines are also worn and damaged but appear to be small and spatulate.

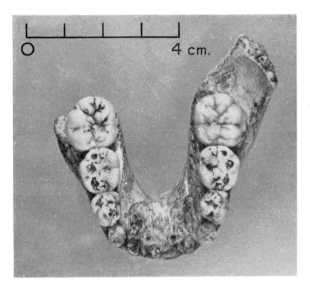

Fig. 62 The Taung mandible
Occlusal view
Courtesy of Professor P. V. Tobias, photographed by A. R. Hughes

The Upper First Deciduous Molars are considerably worn particularly on the lingual half of the crowns, but the mesio-buccal angles of the teeth seem exaggerated in their development.

The Upper Second Deciduous Molars are also worn but enough of the crown morphology is discernible to show that they resemble the first milk molars.

The Upper First Permanent Molars are both perfect. The crowns bear four main cusps and show anterior foveae as well as a Carabelli complex of grooves. These features are characteristic of teeth from Sterkfontein but not of those from Swartkrans.

The Lower Deciduous Incisors are heavily worn and damaged.

The left Lower Deciduous Canine is well preserved and has a   165 distal cusplet. The tooth does not appear to project appreciably above the occlusal line.

The Lower First Deciduous Molars are little damaged and resemble the equivalent teeth from Sterkfontein in some detail: five main cusps are present and the Taung specimens have small sixth cusps.

The Lower Second Deciduous Molars are appreciably worn but the typical dryopithecine cusp pattern can still be defined. Well developed sixth cusps have obliterated the posterior foveae but the anterior foveae are prominent.

The Lower First Permanent Molars are unworn and display five principal cusps, sixth cusps have obliterated the posterior foveae. Deeply incised buccal grooves are present, the anterior ones ending in a distinct pit.

Dimensions   SKULL

Max. Length (Glabella/Inion) 127·0   Cranial Index 62·4
Cranial Capacity approx. 500 cc

TEETH

		Upper Dentition	(Crown Dimensions)				
		DI1	DI2	DC	DM1	DM2	M1 (Perm.)
Left	l	—★	—★	—★	8·8	—★	12·75
side	b	—★	—★	6·0	10·0	—★	14·0
Right	l	—★	—★	6·8	8·8	10·1	12·75
side	b	—★	—★	5·8	10·0	11·0	14·0

		Lower Dentition (Crown Dimensions)					
		DI1	DI2	DC	DM1	DM2	M1 (Perm.)
Left	l	—★	—★	6·5	—★	11·5	14·0
side	b	—★	—★	5·3	—★	10·6	13·5
Right	l	—★	—★	—★	8·7	11·5	14·0
side	b	—★	—★	—★	8·0	10·7	13·5

★ Damaged

Affinities   The affinities of the Taung skull will be discussed with the rest of the australopithecine remains.

Original   Department of Anatomy, Medical School, University of the Witwatersrand, Johannesburg, Republic of South Africa.

The Taung Skull

Casts The University Museum, University of Pennsylvania, Philadelphia 4, Pennsylvania, U.S.A.

References DART, R. A. 1925
Australopithecus africanus: the man-ape of South Africa. *Nature 115,* 195-199.
DART, R. A. 1926
Taungs and its significance. *Nat. Hist. 3,* 315-327.
DART, R. A. 1934
The dentition of *Australopithecus africanus. Folio anat. jap. 12,* 207-221.
BROOM, R., and SCHEPERS, G. W. H. 1946
The South African fossil ape-men, the *Australopithecinae. Transv. Mus. Mem. 2,* 1-272.
MAYR, E. 1950
Taxonomic categories in fossil hominids. *Cold Spring Harbour Symposia on Quantitative Biology 15, 109-118.*
OAKLEY, K. P. 1954
The dating of the *Australopithecinae* of Africa. *Am. J. Phys. Anthrop. 12,* 9-28.
PEABODY, F. E. 1954
Travertines and cave deposits of the Kaap escarpment of South Africa and the type locality of *Australopithecus africanus* Dart. *Bull. geol. Soc. Am. 65,* 671-705.
ROBINSON, J. T. 1954
The genera and species of the *Australopithecinae. Am. J. Phys. Anthrop. 12,* 181-200.
ROBINSON, J. T. 1956
The detention of the *Australopithecinae. Transv. Mus. Mem. 9,* 1-179.
EWER, R. F. 1957
Faunal evidence on the dating of the *Australopithecinae. Proc. Third Pan-African Cong. Prehist., Livingstone, 1955.* Ed. J. D. Clark, pp. 135-142. London: Chatto and Windus.
OAKLEY, K. P. 1957
Dating the australopithecines. *Ibid.,* pp. 155-157.
KURTÉN, B. 1962
The relative ages of the australopithecines of Transvaal and the pithecanthropines of Java. In *Evolution und Hominisation.* Ed. G. Kurth, pp. 74-80. Stuttgart: Gustav Fischer Verlag.
COOKE, H. B. S. 1964
Pleistocene mammal faunas of Africa, with particular reference to South Africa. In *African ecology and human evolution.* Eds. F. C. Howell and F. Bourlière, pp. 65-116. London: Methuen and Co. Ltd.
OAKLEY, K. P. 1964
Frameworks for dating fossil man. London: Weidenfeld and Nicolson.

The Sterkfontein Remains

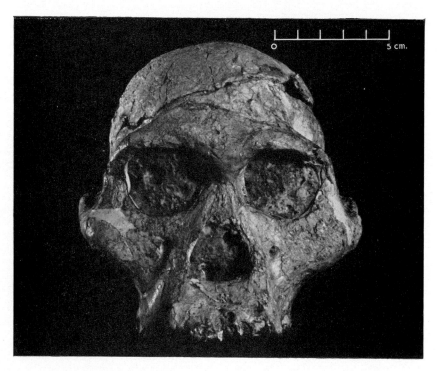

Fig. 63   Sterkfontein skull 5 ('Plesianthropus 5')
Frontal view
Courtesy of Professor J. T. Robinson

*Synonyms
and other names*   *Australopithecus transvaalensis* (Broom, 1936); *Plesianthropus transvaalensis* (Broom, 1937); *Homo transvaalensis* (Mayr, 1950); *Australopithecus (Plesianthropus) transvaalensis* (Oakley, 1954); *Australopithecus africanus transvaalensis* (Robinson, 1954) 'Ape-man'; 'Man-ape'; 'Near-man'

Site   Sterkfontein Type Site and Sterkfontein Extension Site, seven miles north-west of Krugersdorp, near Johannesburg, Transvaal, Republic of South Africa.

Found by   1. R. Broom, August, 1936 (Cranial and post-cranial bones, teeth).
2. R. Broom and J. T. Robinson, 1947–1948 (Cranial and post-cranial bones, teeth).

168

The majority of the hominid material is derived from the Type Site.

Geology   At Sterkfontein a number of caves honeycomb a Pre-Cambrian formation of impure dolomitic limestone. The cave fillings consist of calcareous bone breccia that has been mined for many years and burned in kilns for lime. The principal site is the remains of a large cavern which communicates with the surface; gradually it had become filled with debris and bones until the cavern floor collapsed into an underlying cavity in the rock. The process then recurred, the new cavern again filling from above. Because of this mode of formation, the breccia is not of uniform character, neither is it regularly stratified. The geology of Sterkfontein has been investigated in detail (Brain, 1957, 1958; Robinson and Mason, 1962).

Associated finds   A number of stone tools have been recovered from the Extension Site (Robinson, 1957; Brain, 1958; Robinson and Mason, 1962). They comprise two hand-axes, choppers, flakes, irregular artefacts and a spheroid. The tools are made of diabase, quartzite or chert. The culture has been described as Late Oldowan or Early Chelles-Acheul in character, and has been attributed to later pithecanthropines who may have occupied the site (Robinson and Mason, 1962).

The fossil mammalian fauna recovered from Sterkfontein Type Site include insectivores (*Chlorotalpa spelaea, Elephantulus langi, Crocidura* cf. *bicolor, Suncus etruscus, Myosorex robinsoni*), primates (*Parapapio jonesi, P. broomi, P. whitei, Cercopithecoides williamsi*), numerous rodents, some carnivores (*Canis mesomelas pappos, Canis brevirostris, Lycyaena silbergi, Therailurus barlowi, Megantereon gracile*), hyraces (*Procavia antiqua, P. transvaalensis*) and some artiodactyls ('*Tapinochoerus*' *meadowsi, Hippotragus broomi, Gazella wellsi*) (Cooke, 1964). The presence of an equid (*Equus*) at the Extension Site has been reported (Robinson, 1958).

Dating   The same difficulties arise in dating the Sterkfontein sites as were encountered at the other australopithecine sites; the problem has been discussed by a number of authors (Howell, 1955; Ewer, 1957; Oakley, 1954, 1957; Brain, 1958; Robinson and Mason, 1962). Kurtén (1962) attributed the Sterkfontein remains to the First Interglacial (Günz–Mindel or

Antepenultimate Interglacial) on the grounds of faunal correlation. However, in general it is agreed that the Sterkfontein Type Site deposits belong to the early part of the sequence of australopithecine sites—the Upper Villafranchian portion of the Lower Pleistocene.

Morphology The earlier excavation produced a broken cranium, maxillary, zygomatic and nasal bones, some mandibular fragments,

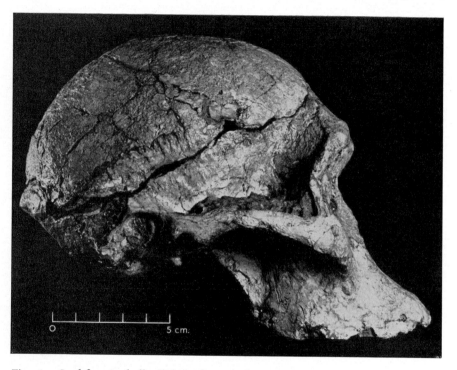

Fig. 64 Sterkfontein skull 5 ('Plesianthropus 5')
Right lateral view
Courtesy of Professor J. T. Robinson

socketed and isolated teeth, the lower end of a left femur and a capitate. The later excavation was rewarded by an almost complete cranium, several other damaged and incomplete crania, a nearly complete mandible, parts of other mandibles, several maxillae, numerous socketed and isolated teeth, part of a scapula, the upper end of a humerus, vertebrae, ribs, right

170

and left innominate bones, the proximal end of a femur and the distal end of a femur.

Subsequently further material has come to light including a complete dentition, a sacrum and a second femoral fragment, almost identical to the first but of the opposite side.

SKULL

The best-preserved cranium, Skull 5, is that of a mature female widely known colloquially as 'Mrs Ples'; it is virtually complete, lacking only the upper teeth. The vault is rounded and marked anteriorly by a modest supra-orbital ridge and some prominence of the glabella. The occipital crest is weak and the nuchal plane low. The foramen magnum is set well beneath the cranium and the mastoid processes are small. The greatest breadth of the cranium is bitemporal,

MANDIBLE

The more complete mandible is rather crushed, particularly on the right side; most of the teeth are preserved but they are heavily worn. The jaw is large and robust, the symphysial region is well preserved and there is neither chin nor simian shelf. The body of the mandible is stout and the rami are tall.

PERMANENT TEETH

Over 120 permanent teeth are known from Sterkfontein.

The Upper Incisors are small and moderately shovelled, having marginal ridges on their lingual faces.

The Upper Canines are symmetrical and pointed, projecting a little beyond the adjacent teeth; the lingual face of these teeth have parallel grooves whilst two specimens have small lingual tubercles.

The Upper First Premolars are bicuspid and have well defined buccal grooves. The roots are poorly developed.

The Upper Second Premolars are all worn but resemble the first premolars in having the same occlusal features and buccal grooves. The roots tend to be narrow.

The Upper First Molars are rhomboid in shape, having a simple quadrituberculate cusp pattern. A Carabelli complex seems to be a constant feature of these teeth.

The Upper Second Molars are similar to the first molars but slightly larger. Characteristically a well developed cingulum is present running from the lingual groove to the lingual end of the mesial face. An extra cusp is often found distally.　171

The Upper Third Molars are essentially the same size and shape as the second molars, having a lingual groove and part of a Carabelli complex. The fissure pattern of the occlusal surface is complicated.

★   ★   ★

The Lower Incisors tend to be shovelled and have horizontal incisal margins. Both central and lateral specimens have five well developed mamelons.

The Lower Canines differ considerably from the upper in that the crown is always asymmetrical; the apex of the tooth is distal to its midline and the cingulum reaches higher up the mesial face than the distal face. The cingulum on the distal face forms a distinct cusplet.

The Lower First and Second Premolar crowns are bicuspid and asymmetrical. The lingual cusp is smaller than the buccal cusp, and the anterior and posterior foveae are well defined.

The Lower First Molars are rectangular having five cusps and a larger anterior fovea.

The Lower Second Molars have six cusps and a moderate anterior fovea.

The Lower Third Molars tend to be triangular; they usually have six cusps and a distinct anterior fovea.

DECIDUOUS TEETH

The Upper First Molar is asymmetrical due to the large mesio-buccal angle of its crown; a fifth cusp is present.

The Upper Second Molar is similar in form to the first permanent molar and has a distinct Carabelli cusp.

★   ★   ★

The Lower Incisors are either damaged or worn.

The Lower Canine has a moderately high crown with distal and mesial cusplets.

The Lower First Molar has five cusps and a large anterior fovea.

The Lower Second Molar has a similar cusp arrangement to the first permanent molar.

THE POST-CRANIAL BONES

The Scapula is a little crushed and has lost its lower and inner half. The neck of the bone is not clearly defined and there is no scapula notch. Its principal resemblances are said to be with man and the orang-utan.

The Humerus belongs to the same individual as the scapula and

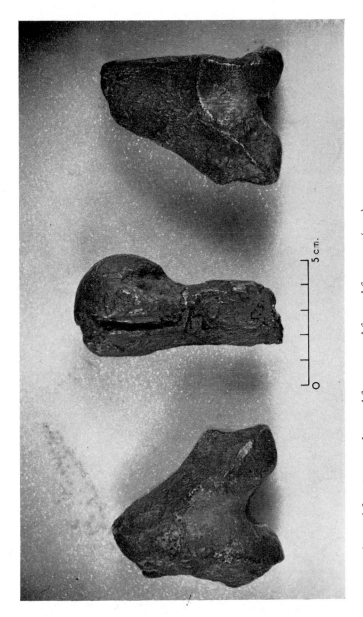

Fig. 65 The Sterkfontein upper humeral fragment and femoral fragments (casts)

has the head and upper end of the shaft in good condition. The remainder of the shaft is badly crushed, and the lower end is missing. The head of the bone is very like that of modern man, having greater and lesser tuberosities separated by an intertubercular groove and a well rounded articular surface.

Of the two *Innominate Bones* the right one is almost complete; the acetabulum is perfect and undistorted but the ischium and part of the pubis have been crushed. The ilium is broad and similar to that of man, but the anterior superior spine extends farther forward and the iliac crest is less curved than in most human ilia. The iliac pillar, which in man extends from the acetabulum to the tubercle of the crest, is feeble and runs forward to the anterior superior iliac spine. The sacral articulation

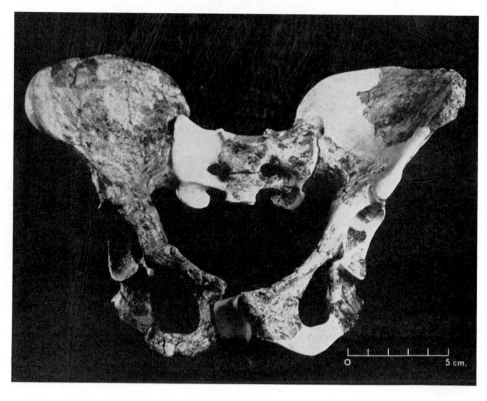

Fig. 66   The Sterkfontein pelvis (restored)
Courtesy of Professor J. T. Robinson

is small, as is the roughened region above for the sacro-iliac ligaments. The ischial tuberosity, which is irregular and flattened, is set well away from the edge of the acetabulum to produce a strikingly long pelvic ischial segment. The orientation of the pelvis is distinctive; in man the iliac crests are mainly directed forwards, but in this form they were mainly directed laterally.

Closely associated with the pelvis was much of the left *Femur*, but while its upper end is fairly well preserved the shaft is crushed. The head of the bone is well rounded, the trochanteric fossa small and the lesser trochanter backwardly directed. Two other fragments, the lower ends of right and left femora, are very similar in size and shape. They closely resemble the femur of man but differ in the relative depth and forward extension of their intercondylar grooves.

The Capitate Bone and a *Phalangeal Fragment* were recovered during the early excavation. The capitate is small and similar to that of man in its essential features.

The remaining post-cranial bones have not yet been described.

Dimensions SKULL

Broom, Robinson and Schepers (1950)

Skull 5 Max. Length 146·8   Max. Breadth 99·0

Cranial Index 67·5   Cranial Capacity 482 cc

MANDIBLE

Body Thickness at M1 24·0   Body Depth at M1 37·0

Coronoid Height 86·5   Minimum Ramus Breadth *c.* 60·0

TEETH

Robinson (1956)

Sts 52a		Upper Permanent Teeth (Crown Dimensions)							
		I1	I2	C	PM1	PM2	M1	M2	M3
Left	l	9·5	7·3	9·8	8·7	9·1	12·3	13·2	—
Side	b	8·2	7·0	9·9	12·8	(13·2)	14·0	15·2	—
Right	l	9·3	6·8	9·9	8·6	9·3	12·2	13·3	12·5
Side	b	8·3	7·0	9·7	12·8	13·3	14·1	15·2	14·6

Sts 52b		Lower Permanent Teeth (Crown Dimensions)							
Left	l	—	—	—	—	—	13·4	14·8	13·5
Side	b	—	—	—	—	—	13·3	12·9	
Right	l	5·9	7·1	9·1	9·0	9·8	13·0	14·4	13·7
Side	b	8·1	8·1	10·0	11·7	11·7	12·9	13·4	12·7

175

Sts 2		Upper Deciduous Teeth (Crown Dimensions)				
		DI1	DI2	DC	DM1	DM2
Left	l	—	—	—	—	—
Side	b	—	—	—	—	—
Right	l	—	—	—	9·9	11·2
Side	b	—	—	—	9·6	11·3

Sts 24		Lower Deciduous Teeth (Crown Dimensions)				
Left	l	4·2	—	6·4	—	—
Side	b	—	—	5·6	—	—
Right	l	—	—	6·3	8·2	10·7
Side	b	—	—	5·6	6·9	9·0

POST-CRANIAL BONES

Scapula: Glenoid Cavity Max. Length *c.* 33

Max. Breadth 20

Humerus: Diameter of Head *c.* 40

Length Between 290 and 310

Innominate Bone: Ant. Sup. Spine–Post. Sup. Spine *c.* 115

Sacral articulation, Max. Length 29

Femur: Max. Length *c.* 310

Affinities The affinities of the Sterkfontein remains will be discussed with the rest of the australopithecine material.

Originals The Transvaal Museum, Pretoria, Republic of South Africa.

Casts The University Museum, University of Pennsylvania, Philadelphia 4, Pennsylvania, U.S.A. (Proximal end of right humerus, innominate bone, distal ends of right and left femora.)

References BROOM, R. 1936
A new fossil anthropoid skull from South Africa. *Nature 138*, 486-488.
BROOM, R. 1937
The Sterkfontein ape. *Nature 139*, 326.
BROOM, R. and SCHEPERS, G. W. H. 1946
The South African fossil ape-men, the *Australopithecinae*. *Transv. Mus. Mem. 2*, 1-272.
KERN, H. M. and STRAUS, W. L. 1949
The femur of *Plesianthropus transvaalensis*. *Am. J. Phys. anthrop. 7*, 53-77.

BROOM, R., ROBINSON, J. T., and SCHEPERS, G. W. H. 1950
Sterkfontein ape-man, *Plesianthropus. Transv. Mus. Mem. 4*, 1-117.
MAYR, E. 1950
Taxonomic categories in fossil hominids. *Cold Spring Harbour Symposia on Quantitative Biology 15*, 109-118.
OAKLEY, K. P. 1954
Dating the australopithecines of Africa. *Am. J. Phys. Anthrop. 12*, 9-23.
ROBINSON, J. T. 1954
The genera and species of the *Australopithecinae. Am. J. Phys. Anthrop. 12*, 181-200.
HOWELL, F. C. 1955
The age of the australopithecines of Southern Africa. *Am. J. Phys. Anthrop. 13*, 635-662.
ROBINSON, J. T. 1956
The dentition of the *Australopithecinae. Transv. Mus. Mem. 9*, 1-179.
BRAIN, C. K. 1957
New evidence for the correlation of the Transvaal ape-man bearing cave deposits. *Proc. Third. Pan-African Cong. Prehist., Livingstone, 1955.* Ed. J. D. Clark, pp. 143-148. London: Chatto and Windus.
EWER, R. F. 1957
Faunal evidence on the dating of the *Australopithecinae. Ibid.*, pp. 135-142.
OAKLEY, K. P. 1957
Dating the australopithecines. *Ibid.*, pp. 155-157.
ROBINSON, J. T., and MASON, R. J. 1957
Occurrence of stone artefacts with *Australopithecus* at Sterkfontein. *Nature 180*, 521-524.
BRAIN, C. K. 1958
The Transvaal ape-man bearing cave deposits. *Transv. Mus. Mem. 11*, 1-125.
ROBINSON, J. T., 1958
The Sterkfontein tool-maker. *The Leech (Johannesburg) 28*, 94-100.
ROBSINSON, J. T., and MASON, R. J. 1962
Australopithecines and artefacts at Sterkfontein. *S. Afr. Arch. Bull. 17*, 87-125.
KURTÉN, B. 1962
The relative ages of the australopithecines of Transvaal and the pithecanthropines of Java. In *Evolution und Hominisation*. Ed. G. Kurth, pp. 74-80. Stuttgart: Gustav Fischer Verlag.
COOKE, H. B. S. 1964
Pleistocene mammal faunas of Africa, with particular reference to South Africa. In *African ecology and human evolution*. Eds. F. C. Howell and F. Boulière, pp. 65-116. London: Methuen and Co. Ltd.

N FM

The Kromdraai Remains

Synonyms and other names	*Paranthropus robustus* (Broom, 1938); *Homo transvaalensis* (Mayr, 1950); *Paranthropus robustus robustus* (Robinson, 1954); *Australopithecus robustus* (Oakley, 1954); *Australopithecus robustus robustus* (Campbell, 1964) 'Near-man'; 'Ape-man'; 'Man-ape'
Site	Kromdraai, two miles east of Sterkfontein, nine miles north-west of Krugersdorp, near Johannesburg, Transvaal, Republic of South Africa.
Found by	(a) G. Terblanche, June, 1938; recognized by R. Broom. Cranial and post-cranial bones. (b) R. Broom, February, 1941. Juvenile mandible.
Geology	The bones were found in a block of stony breccia loose on the surface of the hillside at a point later named Kromdraai B. Excavation showed that this block was derived from the filling of a cave, formed in Pre-Cambrian dolomitic limestone, whose roof had completely weathered away. A similar cave-filling near by, Kromdraai A, has yielded quantities of mammalian fossil bones but no hominid material. The geology of the site has been investigated in detail (Brain, 1957, 1958).
Associated finds	One unquestionable chert artefact has been claimed from Kromdraai B and four other specimens from the same site regarded as less convincing stone tools (Brain, 1958). Until more evidence is available it would be unwise to classify these implements as a recognizable culture.
	Fossil mammalian bones recovered from Kromdraai A include insectivores (*Proamblysomus antiquus, Elephantulus langi, Crocidura cf. bicolor, Suncus cf. etruscus*), primates (*Gorgopithecus major, Parapapio jonesi, Papio angusticeps, Papio robinsoni*), a number of extinct rodents, several large and small carnivores (*Canis terblanchei, Herpestes mesotes, Crocuta spelaea, Crocuta ultra, Felis crassidens, Panthera shawi*), elephant (*Loxodonta atlantica*), hyraces (*Procavia antiqua, P. transvaalensis*), equids (*Stylohipparion steytleri, Equus plicatus, Equus helmei*) and a pig (*Potamochoerops antiquus*) (Cooke, 1964).
Dating	The fossil bones recovered from Kromdraai cannot at present

178

be dated by direct chemical or radiometric methods since they were preserved in limestone; assessments of their ages must rely therefore on geological and faunal evidence.

Unfortunately the cave deposit is not clearly stratified, and the artefacts that were found do not form part of an established sequence. Faunal dating also presents problems in South Africa since the Plio-Pleistocene boundary is not clearly defined by a change in the composition of the fauna (Ewer, 1957). Kurtén (1962) attributed the Kromdraai deposit to the Second Glaciation (Mindel or Antepenultimate Glaciation), on the grounds of faunal correlation.

However, Kromdraai is commonly regarded as one of the most recent of the Transvaal australopithecine sites and has been attributed to the Basal Middle Pleistocene (Oakley, 1954, 1964).

Morphology   The fossil hominid bones recovered from Kromdraai B comprise the left half of a cranium including the left maxilla and zygomatic bones, part of the left sphenoid, the left temporal, a fragmentary right maxilla, the right half of the body of a mandible, three isolated molars and four premolars. In addition some post-cranial bones were found including the distal end of a right humerus, the proximal end of a right ulna, a metacarpal, a proximal finger phalanx, a broken talus and two toe phalanges. Later, a juvenile mandible was found containing most of the deciduous teeth and the right first permanent molar.

SKULL

The skull is heavily built, having a relatively large face and a small cranium; the infra-temporal fossa is deep, suggesting marked post-orbital constriction. The brow ridges are absent but it seems likely that they were prominent, rather than exaggerated.

The position of the foramen magnum is well beneath the skull, and the mastoid process is small. The glenoid fossa is broad and shallow, bounded in front by an articular eminence and behind by a modest post-glenoid tubercle. This arrangement suggests a temporo-mandibular mechanism of human character, a concept borne out by the nature of the wear of the teeth. The tympanic bone is broad and flat, forming the posterior wall of the articular fossa.

179

The maxilla is broad and flat, bearing a single infra-orbital foramen; there is no sign of a maxillo-premaxillary suture on the anterior aspect of the maxilla which is moderately prognathic. The mandible is represented by the anterior two-thirds of the body on the right side; this is very stout and bears the premolar and molar teeth. There is neither pronounced mandibular torus nor chin and the mental foramina are multiple.

PERMANENT TEETH

The Upper Incisors and Canines are lost but the second incisor and canine sockets are small.

The First Upper Premolars are large and have two rounded cusps separated by a fissure; there is a well marked posterior fovea. The socketed specimen has two buccal roots and a lingual root.

The Second Upper Premolars are similar to the first premolars but a little larger; they also have three roots.

The Upper First Molar is irregularly rhomboidal in shape, has four cusps and no trace of a Carabelli complex.

The Upper Second Molars are four-cusped and similar in shape to the first molars.

The Upper Third Molars are basically four-cusped: the arrangement of the cusps is somewhat simplified.

★　　　　　★　　　　　★

The Lower Incisor and Canine Teeth are missing but their sockets in a symphysial fragment are remarkably small.

The Lower First Premolars are large with two main cusps which are low and rounded. The anterior fovea is deep and there is no cingulum.

The Lower Second Premolars are large and bicuspid, perhaps tending to be molariform.

The Lower First Molars are represented by a worn specimen in the type jaw, and an incompletely erupted specimen in the juvenile mandible. The worn specimen has five cusps and a small sixth cusp, whereas the other tooth is small and has no sixth cusp.

The Lower Second Molar is broken but appears to be larger than the first molar; the cusps show evidence of flat wear.

The Lower Third Molar is in the mandible and is well preserved; it has six cusps and is larger than the other two molars.　　180

DECIDUOUS TEETH

These teeth are known from the mandible of a juvenile whose dental age has been estimated at about three to four years.

The First Lower Deciduous Incisor is absent.

The Second Lower Deciduous Incisor is small and very like the corresponding human tooth.

The Lower Deciduous Canine has a very small crown with a moderately well defined cingulum, and mesial and distal cusplets.

The First Deciduous Molars are both present and unworn. They appear to be remarkably human in their shape and cusp pattern.

The Second Deciduous Molar is rather elongated mesio-distally, has five main cusps and a rudimentary sixth cusp.

POST-CRANIAL BONES

The Lower Extremity of the Right Humerus is well preserved and remarkably human in its general shape. The capitulum is rounded but set a little farther back than is usual in modern man. The medial epicondyle is rather pointed but is marked

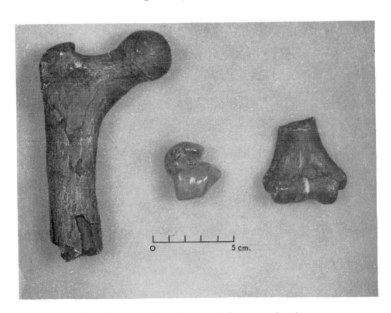

Fig. 67   *Right*—The Kromdraai humeral fragment (cast)
            Centre—The Kromdraai talus (cast)
            Left—The Swartkrans femur, SK 82 (cast) (see page 191)

for the attachment of the flexor muscles of the forearm. The lateral epicondyle is similarly marked for the extensor muscles. According to Le Gros Clark (1947) the humerus has none of the distinctive features found in the recent anthropoid apes; however, this view is not shared by Straus (1948) who suggests that this humerus is 'no more hominid than anthropoid' and believes that its principal affinities are with man *and* chimpanzee. *The Ulnar Fragment* was found near the end of the humerus and almost certainly belongs with it; it resembles that of modern man. The olecranon process is small, suggesting that the range of elbow extension was full.

The hand bones consist of the distal two-thirds of a *Left Second Metacarpal* which is larger than its human counterpart and has two palmar sesamoid grooves on its head. The *Proximal Finger Phalanx*, which probably belongs with the metacarpal, is also grooved for sesamoids.

The Talus lacks the lower part of the body and head. It is a small bone with a narrow superior articular surface but a broad head and short neck. The horizontal angle of the neck is high by comparison with modern man. The broadness of the head of the bone and its position relative to the body has led to the suggestion that the hallux may have been capable of prehensile divergence as well as close alignment with the other toes in walking and standing (Le Gros Clark, 1947).

The Toe Phalanges have been described as a left fifth proximal phalanx (damaged) and a second or third distal phalanx.

Dimensions　SKULL

Broom and Schepers (1946)

Cranial Capacity 650 cc (estimated)

MANDIBLE

Body Thickness (PM2) 23·4

TEETH

Robinson (1956)

		Upper Permanent Teeth (Crown Dimensions)							
		I1	I2	C	PM1	PM2	M1	M2	M3
Left	l	—	—	—	10·0	10·3	13·7	13·8	14·4
side	b	—	—	—	13·7	15·2	14·6	15·9	16·2
Right	l	—	—	—	10·2	—	—	13·8	14·2
side	b	—	—	—	—	—	—	15·9	16·1

		Lower Permanent Teeth (Crown Dimensions)							
		I1	I2	C	PM1	PM2	M1	M2	M3
Left	l	—	—	—	10·0	11·1	—	—	—
side	b	—	—	—	12·2	13·0	—	—	—
Right	l	—	—	—	—	11·0	14·4	—	16·4
side	b	—	—	—	—	13·1	13·0	—	14·0

		Lower Deciduous Teeth (Crown Dimensions)					
		DI1	DI2	DC	DM1	DM2	M1 (Perm.)
Left	l	—	—	—	9·7	12·5★	—
side	b	—	—	—	8·1	10·0	—
Right	l	—	4·6	5·2	9·7	11·6	12·7
side	b	—	3·7	4·9	8·1	9·7	11·5

★ Damaged

POST-CRANIAL BONES

Broom and Schepers (1946)

Humerus: Bicondylar Width 54·0
           Max. Width of Articular Surface 40·0

Metacarpal: Length approx. 70·0
           Width of Head 12·0

Proximal Phalanx (? Left 2nd finger): Length 45·0

Distal Phalanx (? 2nd or 3rd toe): Length 12·5
           Width of proximal end 8·3

Talus (taken from a cast)
    Length 34·5
    Breadth 28·5
    Length/Breadth Index 82·6
    Horizontal Angle of Neck 30°
    Torsion of Neck approx. 30°

Humerus (Straus, 1948; from a cast)
    Bicondylar Width 54·0
    Width of the Trochlear 20·0
    Depth of the Trochlear 23·0
    Width of the Capitulum 16·0
    Max. Width of Articular Surface 40·0

Affinities The affinities of the Kromdraai remains will be discussed with the rest of the australopithecine material.

Originals The Transvaal Museum, Pretoria, Republic of South Africa.

Casts The University Museum, University of Pennsylvania, Philadelphia 4, Pennsylvania, U.S.A.

References BROOM, R. 1938
The Pleistocene anthropoid apes of South Africa. *Nature 142*, 377-379.

BROOM, R. and SCHEPERS, G. W. H. 1946
The South African fossil ape-men, the *Australopithecinae. Transv. Mus. Mem. 2*, 1-272.

CLARK, W. E. LE GROS 1947
Observations on the anatomy of the fossil *Australopithecinae. J. Anat. (Lond.) 81*, 300-333.

STRAUS, W. L. JNR. 1948
The humerus of *Paranthropus robustus. Am. J. Phys. Anthrop. 6*, 285-311.

MAYR, E. 1950
Taxonomic categories in fossil hominids. *Cold Spring Harbour Symposia on Quantitative Biology 15*, 109-118.

OAKLEY, K. P. 1954
Dating the australopithecines of Africa. *Am. J. Phys. Anthrop. 12*, 9-23.

ROBINSON, J. T. 1954
The genera and species of the *Australopithecinae. Am. J. Phys. Anthrop. 12*, 181-200.

ROBINSON, J. T. 1956
The dentition of the *Australopithecinae. Transv. Mus. Mem. 9*, 1-179.

BRAIN, C. K. 1957
New evidence for the correlation of the Transvaal ape-man bearing cave deposits. *Proc. Third Pan-African Cong. Prehist., Livingstone 1955.* Ed. J. D. Clark, pp. 143-148. London: Chatto and Windus.

EWER, R. F. 1957
Faunal evidence on the dating of the *Australopithecinae. Ibid.*, pp. 135-142.

BRAIN, C. K. 1958
The Transvaal ape-man bearing cave deposits. *Transv. Mus. Mem. 11*, 1-125.

KURTÉN, B. 1962
The relative ages of the australopithecines of Transvaal and the pithecanthropines of Java. In *Evolution und Hominisation.* Ed. G. Kurth, pp. 74-80. Stuttgart: Gustav Fischer Verlag.

OAKLEY, K. P. 1964
Frameworks for dating fossil man, p. 291. London: Weidenfeld and Nicolson.

CAMPBELL, B. 1964
Quantitative taxonomy and human evolution. In *Classification and human evolution.* Ed. S. L. Washburn, pp. 50-74. London: Methuen and Co. Ltd.

COOKE, H. B. S. 1964
Pleistocene mammal faunas of Africa, with particular reference to South Africa. In *African ecology and human evolution.* Eds. F. C. Howell and F. Boulière, pp. 65-116. London: Methuen and Co. Ltd.

The Swartkrans Remains

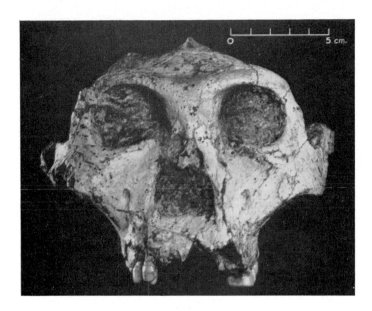

Fig. 68   A skull from Swartkrans, SK 48
Frontal view
Courtesy of Professor J. T. Robinson

Synonyms   1. *Paranthropus crassidens* (Broom, 1949); *Homo transvaalensis*
and other   (Mayr, 1950); *Australopithecus (Paranthropus) crassidens* (Oakley,
names   1954); *Paranthropus robustus crassidens* (Robinson, 1954);
Australopithecus robustus crassidens (Campbell, 1964)
'Ape-man'; 'Man-ape'; 'Near-man'
2. *Telanthropus capensis* (Broom and Robinson, 1949); *Pithecanthropus capensis* (Simonetta, 1957); *Homo erectus* (Robinson,
1961); *Australopithecus capensis* (Oakley, 1964)

Site   Swartkrans, six miles north-west of Krugersdorp, near
Johannesburg, Republic of South Africa.

Found by   1. R. Broom, November, 1948–1951; J. T. Robinson, 1948–
1952.
2. J. T. Robinson, April 1949.

Geology   The Swartkrans site is situated near to the Sterkfontein and
Kromdraai excavations and consists of the remains of a cavern   185

in Pre-Cambrian dolomitic limestone. The roof of the outer part of the cave has been removed by erosion but the inner cave is still protected by a thick layer of dolomite. The cavern appears to have originated from subsidence of the deposit into an underlying solution cavity.

The cave-filling is made up of two types of breccia, pink and brown, above a layer of dripstone. The younger brown breccia of the inner cave overlies the older pink breccia of the outer cave unconformably. The pink breccia contained nearly all of the hominid fossils and is unstratified, whereas the brown breccia contained comparatively little fossil bone and is well stratified. The geology of the site has been investigated in detail (Brain, 1958).

Associated finds   Several quartzite artefacts were recovered from the dumps of breccia which surrounded the excavation. They appear to be of Oldowan type but too few were recovered to allow a definite cultural assessment.

The fossil mammalian bones that were found include those of insectivores (*Chlorotalpa spelea, Elephantulus langi, Elephantulus cf. brachyrhynchus, Suncus cf. etruscus*), primates (*Simopithecus danieli, Parapapio jonesi, Papio robinsoni, Dinopithecus ingens, Cercopithecoides williamsi*), rodents (*Dasymys bolti, Palaeotomys gracilis, Cryptomys robertsi*), several carnivores (*Canis meso-melas pappos, Cynictis penicillata, Lycyaena silbergi, Lycyaena nitidula, Leecyaena forfex, Crocuta crocuta angella, Crocuta venustula, Hyaena brunnea, H. brunnea dispar, Panthera* aff. *leo, P. pardus incurva, Megantereon eurynodon*), hyraces (*Procavia antiqua, P. transvaalensis*) and two artiodactyls ('*Tapinochoerus*' *meadowsi, Potamochoerops antiquus*) (Cooke, 1964).

Dating   The nature of the deposit at Swartkrans precludes chemical or radiometric dating with the techniques available at present. The dating problem has been discussed by a number of authors (Howell, 1955; Ewer, 1957; Oakley, 1954, 1957; Brain, 1958). Kurtén (1962) has suggested recently that all the Transvaal australopithecine sites are post-Villafranchian and that Swartkrans should be attributed to the Second Glaciation (Mindel Glaciation or Antepenultimate Glaciation) with Kromdraai, on the grounds of faunal correlation. This later date remains to be established since the balance of faunal and geological evidence seems to indicate a Basal Middle Pleistocene age for both of these sites (Oakley, 1954, 1964).

Morphology The remains from Swartkrans comprise:

1. An almost complete cranium, the left half of a cranium with both maxillae, a juvenile cranium, an adolescent cranium and several other crania which have been crushed during fossilization. A number of specimens of maxillae, with most of the upper dentition, were recovered as well as three adult mandibles. Several other mandibles were found, both adult and juvenile, and about 100 isolated teeth. The post-cranial bones include the crushed lower end of a humerus, a left thumb metacarpal, an incomplete innominate bone and the proximal ends of two right femora.

2. A mandible (Telanthropus I), a mandibular fragment (Telanthropus II) containing two molar teeth, a premaxillary fragment (Telanthropus III), an isolated lower first premolar, the proximal end of a radius and the distal end of a fourth left metacarpal.

Fig. 69   A skull from Swartkrans, SK 48
          Left lateral view
          Courtesy of Professor J. T. Robinson

187

The Swartkrans Remains

I. SKULL

The best cranium (SK 48) obtained from Swartkrans is probably that of a female; it is somewhat crushed and was broken during excavation. The supra-orbital ridge is well marked, particularly in the midline, showing a prominent glabella; the forehead is concave and restricted by the union of the temporal lines forming a sagittal crest. The brain-case is small in relation to the size of the facial skeleton, and constricted behind the orbits. Posteriorly the occipital region is damaged but the occipital crest is well defined. The glenoid fossa is deep and bounded posteriorly by the tympanic bone.

The maxillae are robust and flat, separated by a broad nasal opening, but the premaxillary region is shortened giving the dental arcade a 'squared-off' appearance. The palate is large and bounded by stout alveolar processes of bone bearing three molars on the left side and the first premolar and canine on the right.

MANDIBLE

The best-preserved mandible (SK 23) is a fine specimen, virtually complete, with an almost perfect adult dentition.

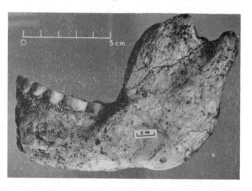

Fig. 70   A mandible from Swartkrans,
SK 23
*Courtesy of Professor J. T.
Robinson*

The only damage it has sustained is some crushing of the body which has resulted in fracture of the symphysial region and narrowing of the dental arcade. This specimen is probably female since two other jaws from Swartkrans are similar in their general features but are even more massive.

The body of the female mandible is stout; the ramus is very tall and buttressed internally by paired ridges running to the coronoid and condyloid processes from the *crista pharyngea*, 188 a crest which runs upwards from the lingual side of the third molar. The symphysial region, although broken, shows that there is neither chin nor true simian shelf, but there is a genio-glossal fossa internally in the midline below the flattened alveolar plane. The internal mandibular torus is of moderate size; externally the anterior border of the coronoid process runs down on to the body as a ridge which passes below the molar teeth and fades away beneath the single mental foramen.

PERMANENT TEETH

273 permanent teeth are known from Swartkrans.

The Upper Incisors are relatively small and shovel-shaped with raised marginal ridges. The lateral incisors tend to be smaller than the central incisors.

The Upper Canines are small-crowned and stout-rooted; they are symmetrical and have blunt points. The lingual faces of these teeth have characteristic grooves.

The Upper First Premolars are bicuspid and asymmetrical in occlusal view; the primary fissure is usually deeply cut.

The Upper Second Premolars resemble the first premolars in cusp pattern but usually have a distinct talon.

The Upper First Molars are characteristically trapezoidal in shape and the crown pattern is simple and four-cusped.

The Upper Second Molars are also skewed in occlusal view and several examples have some of the Carabelli complex.

The Upper Third Molars resemble the second molars in some respects but tend to be even more irregular in shape.

★ ★ ★

The Lower Incisors are relatively simple having horizontal cutting edges; the lateral specimens are slightly shovel-shaped.

The Lower Canines are asymmetrical having a distal cusplet formed by the remnants of the cingulum.

The Lower First Premolars are robust, bicuspid and asymmetrical. The buccal cusp is the larger and it is commonly joined to the lingual cusp by a ridge which separates the anterior and posterior foveae.

The Lower Second Premolar is larger than the first and its crown is partially molarized.

The Lower First Molars are typically hominid in shape; five main cusps are present as well as a small sixth cusp. The fissure pattern is normally dryopithecine with some tendency towards the development of the + pattern typical of modern man. There is some wrinkling of the occlusal enamel.

The Lower Second Molars are similar in shape to the first molars but have four main cusps and a small fifth cusp. The fissure pattern is not dryopithecine and there is some secondary enamel wrinkling.

The Lower Third Molars have complex occlusal cusp patterns and crenelated fissure arrangements. The tooth crowns tend to be of irregular shape.

DECIDUOUS TEETH

The Upper Incisors and Canines are not represented well enough for description.

The Upper First Molar is known from a single specimen, a very worn isolated tooth. The crown is asymmetrical and has four cusps.

The Upper Second Molars, though smaller than the first permanent molars, are very like them in the details of their structure and also have four main cusps.

★   ★   ★

The Lower Incisors are too badly damaged for description.

The Lower Canines have asymmetrical crowns with well marked distal cusplets derived from the cingulum.

The Lower First Molars are well developed and have five cusps separated by the basically dryopithecine fissure system.

The Lower Second Molars are larger than the first and fully molariform. The cusp pattern agrees closely with that of the first molar.

POST-CRANIAL BONES

The Left Thumb Metacarpal (SK 84) is robust, curved and strongly impressed by muscular markings. The distal articular surface is asymmetrical and has a beak-like process separating two sesamoid grooves. The proximal articulation is saddle-shaped.

The Innominate Bone (SK 50) belongs to the right side and lacks the iliac crest, the sacral articulation and most of its pubic portion. The acetabulum is complete but crushing has reduced its anteroposterior diameter. The anterior superior iliac spine is prominent and reaches forwards and laterally; although the

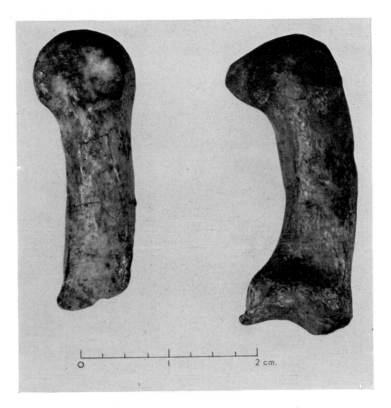

Fig. 71   *Right*—The Swartkrans left thumb metacarpal, SK 84
          Left—The Swartkrans fourth left metacarpal, SK 85

iliac crest is missing it seems likely that it is less sharply
curved than that of man. The ischial segment is long and the
ischial tuberosity well separated from the acetabular margin.
The Upper Ends of Two Femora, both from the right side, are
similar in their principal features. The head is small and
rounded, bearing a sub-central fovea. The neck, broad at the
base, narrows to the articular surface and has an horizontal
upper border. There is a weak trochanteric crest but the
greater trochanter is hollowed by a deep pit towards its apex,
whilst the lesser trochanter is directed posteriorly and medially. The small size of the head by comparison with the thickness of the shaft and the development of the trochanters gives
the bone a disproportionate appearance.   191

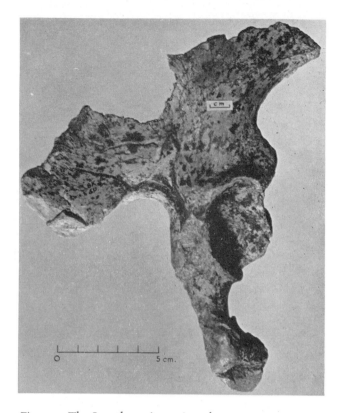

Fig. 72   The Swartkrans innominate bone, SK 50
Courtesy of Professor J. T. Robinson

2. MANDIBLE

In the Swartkrans cave two mandibles were found whose morphology is very different from that of those described in the preceding section. The body of the better specimen (SK 15) is complete and contains five molar teeth, but the ascending rami are broken; the whole jaw is somewhat crushed. The symphysis is almost intact and has neither chin nor simian shelf; internally it is reinforced by a transverse torus below which there is a shallow genioglossal fossa. The body is robust, particularly in the region of the third molar, and the mental foramen on the right side is single.

The second specimen consists of a fragment of the right side of the body of another mandible bearing two molar teeth.   192

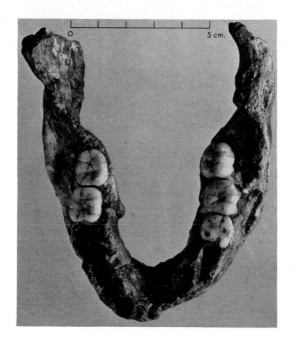

Fig. 73   A mandible from   Swartkrans,   SK 15
(Telanthropus I)
Occlusal view
Courtesy of Professor J. T. Robinson

An isolated premolar tooth was found close to the better mandible.

TEETH

The Premolar is considerably worn but the crown is small and hominid in its general features.

The Left First Molar is intact but worn; however, it is not distinguishable from a modern human lower first molar.

The Second Molars are both worn but it is possible to discern a dryopithecine fissure pattern with six cusps. There seems to be no trace of enamel wrinkling.

The Third Molars are intact and little worn, and resemble the second molars. The dryopithecine fissure pattern (Y_5) is tending towards the + pattern of modern hominids.

POST-CRANIAL BONES

The proximal end of a right *Radius* was recovered with the better mandible. It is said to be indistinguishable from that of

193

modern man although it has never been properly described. The distal end of a fourth left *Metacarpal* (SK 85) was found at Swartkrans. It is not particularly robust, nor does it have any of the specializations associated with pongid metacarpals. Apart from its small size it is similar to the corresponding bone of modern man.

Dimensions 2. SKULL

None of the crania are sufficiently well preserved to allow reliable measurements of their principal dimensions or cranial capacities.

MANDIBLE (SK 23)

Robinson (1953)

Max. Length 127·0

Ramus Height 91 (at coronoid); 84 (at condyle)

Ramus Width 52 and 55 (mid-point)

Body Depth (PM2) 39·7

Body Depth (C) 40·0

Body Depth (M2) 35·7

Body Depth (M3) 33·0

Body Width (M2) 25·0

TEETH

Robinson (1956)

			Upper Permanent Teeth (Crown Dimensions)						
		I_1	I_2	C	PM_1	PM_2	M_1	M_2	M_3
Average	l	9·4	7·2	8·7	9·9	10·6	13·8	14·7	15·1
figures	b	7·6	6·8	9·5	14·2	15·4	14·5	15·9	16·9

SK 23			Lower Permanent Teeth (Crown Dimensions)						
Left	l	5·6	6·7	7·8	9·4	10·5	14·8	15·2	16·0
side	b	5·9	6·7	7·8	11·4	14·1	14·7	14·8	13·0
Right	l	5·6	6·6	8·1	9·6	10·7	14·7	15·0	17·3
side	b	6·3	6·7	8·0	11·5	13·5	14·6	14·8	14·1

		Upper Deciduous Teeth (Crown Dimensions)				
		DI_1	DI_2	DC	DM_1	DM_2
Left	l	—	—	—	—	10·2
side	b	—	—	—	—	12·0
Right	l	—	—	—	8·7	—
side	b	—	—	—	9·8	—
Specimens					SK 91	SK 90

SK 61		*Lower Deciduous Teeth (Crown Dimensions)*				
		DI1	DI2	DC	DM1	DM2
Left	l	—	—	5·7	10·6	13·3
side	b	—	—	5·3	9·5	11·9
Right	l	3·8	4·9	5·9	11·1	13·4
side	b	—	4·6	5·2	9·5	12·0

POST-CRANIAL BONES

The Thumb Metacarpal (SK 84) (Napier, 1959)

Max. Length 35·0   Mid-shaft Breadth 7·5 (A.P.), 9·5 (Transverse)   Robusticity Index 24·3

Femur (SK 82)

Length of neck 63·0 (from a cast)

Mean Thickness of shaft 27·5 (below lesser trochanter) (from a cast)

Mean Diameter of head 33·0 (from a cast)

2. MANDIBLES

Robinson (1953)

Telanthropus I (Restored) (SK 15)

Max. Length 109·0

Body Height (C) 31·5

Body Height (M3) 25·0

Body Width (M2) 22·5

Ramus Height (coronoid) 59·0

Ramus Height (condyle) 55·0

Bicondylar Width 114·0

TEETH

Broom and Robinson (1952)

	Lower Permanent Teeth (Crown Dimensions)			
Telanthropus I (SK 15)	PM1	M1	M2	M3
Left l	8·6	11·9	—	14·3
side b	10·3	11·9	—	12·4
Right l	—	—	13·6	13·9
side b	—	—	13·1	12·3

POST-CRANIAL BONES

Fourth Left Metacarpal (SK 85) (Napier, 1959)

Reconstructed Length 50·7

No dimensions are available for the upper end of the radius.   195

The Swartkrans Remains

Affinities The affinities of the Swartkrans remains will be discussed with the rest of the australopithecine material.

Originals The Transvaal Museum, Pretoria, Republic of South Africa.

Casts The University Museum, University of Pennsylvania, Philadelphia 4, Pennsylvania, U.S.A. 1. Mandible, skull, immature skull, innominate, femora, palate, maxillae. 2. Mandible.

References BROOM, R. 1949
Another new type of fossil ape-man. *Nature 163*, 57.

BROOM, R., and ROBINSON, J. T. 1949
A new type of fossil man. *Nature 164*, 322–323.

BROOM, R., and ROBINSON, J. T. 1950
Man contemporaneous with the Swartkrans ape-man. *Am. J. Phys. Anthrop. 8*, 151–156.

MAYR, E. 1950
Taxonomic categories in fossil hominids. *Cold Spring Harbour Symposia on Quantitative Biology 15*, 109–118.

BROOM, R., and ROBINSON, J. T. 1952
Swartkrans ape-man. *Paranthropus crassidens. Transv. Mus. Mem. 6*, 1–124.

ROBINSON, J. T. 1953
Telanthropus and its phylogenetic significance. *Am. J. Phys. Anthrop. 11*, 445–501.

OAKLEY, K. P. 1954
Dating the australopithecines of Africa. *Am. J. Phys. Anthrop. 12*, 9–23.

ROBINSON, J. T. 1954
The genera and species of the *Australopithecinae. Am. J. Phys. Anthrop. 12*, 181–200.

CLARK, W. E. LE GROS 1955
The *os innominatum* of the recent *Ponginae* with special reference to that of the *Australopithecinae. Am. J. Phys. Anthrop. 13*, 19–27.

DART, R. A. 1955
Australopithecus prometheus and *Telanthropus capensis. Am. J. Phys. Anthrop. 13*, 67–96.

HOWELL, F. C. 1955
The age of the australopithecines of Southern Africa. *Am. J. Phys. Anthrop. 13*, 635–662.

ROBINSON, J. T. 1956
The dentition of the *Australopithecinae. Transv. Mus. Mem. 9*, 1–179.

BRAIN, C. K. 1957
New evidence for the correlation of the Transvaal ape-man bearing cave deposits. *Proc. Third Pan-African Cong. Prehist., Livingstone, 1955*. Ed. J. D. Clark, pp. 143–148. London: Chatto and Windus.

EWER, R. F. 1957
Faunal evidence for the dating of the *Australopithecinae*. *Ibid.*, pp. 135–142.

OAKLEY, K. P. 1957
Dating the australopithecines. *Ibid.*, pp. 155–157.

SIMONETTA, A. 1957
Catalogo e sinominia annotata degli ominoidi fossili ed attuali (1758–1955). *Atti. Soc. tosc. Sci. Nat. 64*, 53–112.

BRAIN, C. K. 1958
The Transvaal ape-man bearing cave deposits. *Transv. Mus. Mem. 11*, 1–125.

NAPIER, J. R. 1959
Fossil metacarpals from Swartkrans. Fossil Mammals of Africa, No. 17. London: British Museum (Nat. Hist.)

ROBINSON, J. T. 1961
The australopithecines and their bearing on the origin of man and of stone tool-making. *S. Afr. J. Sci. 57*, 3–13.

KURTÉN, B. 1962
The relative ages of the australopithecines of Transvaal and the pithecanthropines of Java. In *Evolution und Hominisation*. Ed. G. Kurth, pp. 74–80. Stuttgart: Gustav Fischer Verlag.

CAMPBELL, B. 1964
Quantitative taxonomy and human evolution. In *Classification and human evolution*. Ed. S. L. Washburn, pp. 50–74. London: Methuen and Co. Ltd.

COOKE, H. B. S. 1964
Pleistocene mammal faunas of Africa, with particular reference to South Africa. In *African ecology and human evolution*. Eds. F. C. Howell and F. Bourlière, pp. 65–116. London: Methuen and Co. Ltd.

OAKLEY, K. P. 1964
Frameworks for dating fossil man, p. 291. London: Weidenfeld and Nicolson.

The Makapansgat Remains

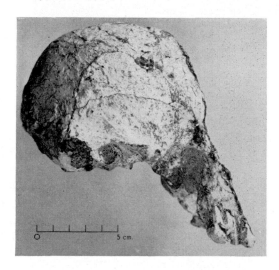

Fig. 74 An incomplete cranium (MLD 37 and MLD 38) from Makapansgat; most of the facial parts have weathered away
Courtesy of Professor P. V. Tobias, photographed by A. R. Hughes

Synonyms
and other names

Australopithecus prometheus (Dart, 1948a); *Homo transvaalensis* (Mayr, 1950); *Australopithecus africanus transvaalensis* (Robinson, 1954)
'Ape-man'; 'Man-ape'; 'Near-man'

Site

Makapansgat Limeworks Dump, Makapansgat Farm, 13 miles north-east of Potgieterus, Central Transvaal, Republic of South Africa.

Found by

Professor R. A. Dart, the staff and students of the Department of Anatomy, University of the Witwatersrand, Johannesburg, and other helpers who included J. Kitching, S. Kitching, B. Kitching, A. R. Hughes, E. L. Boné, R. S. Cunliff and B. Maguire. The finds were made between September 1947 and 1962.

Geology

The limeworks site is situated on the south side of the Makapan valley and consists of a large infilled subsidence cavern which

198

has formed in the Transvaal dolomitic limestone of the region. The major part of the cave roof has eroded away and exposed the consolidated cave breccia on the surface. The bedrock of the cave is covered by a considerable layer of pure dripstone indicating that the cave did not communicate with the surface at the time of its accumulation. When the cave opened to the surface, breccia was formed in two principal phases. Most of the hominid material was found in the lower part of the Phase I breccia. The geology of the site has been studied in detail (King, 1951; Brain, 1958).

Associated finds Numerous utilized bones, teeth and horns have been claimed from the vast accumulation of fossil material from these deposits (Dart, 1957a). Opinion is divided as to whether their appearance is artefactual or natural.

The fossil mammalian fauna recovered from this site includes a bat (*Rhinolophus cf. capensis*), primates (*Simopithecus darti, Parapapio jonesi, P. broomi, P. whitei, Cercopithecoides williamsi*), numerous rodents, some carnivores (*Cynictis penicillata brachydon, Crocuta cf. brevirostris, Hyaena makapani, Therailurus barlowi, Megantereon sp. nov.*), an equid (*Equus helmei*), perissodactyla (*cf. Ceratotherium simum, cf. Diceros bicornis*) and numerous artiodactyls including antelopes, gazelles, pigs and giraffes (Cooke, 1964).

Dating As with the other australopithecine sites in the Transvaal, accurate dating has proved difficult because of the nature of the deposits; the problem has been discussed by several authors (Howell, 1955; Ewer, 1957; Oakley, 1954, 1957; Brain, 1958). Recently the Makapansgat site has been attributed to the First Interglacial (Günz–Mindel or Antepenultimate Interglacial) on the grounds of faunal correlation (Kurtén, 1962); however, most authors agree that Makapansgat is one of the earlier Transvaal sites which, with Taung and Sterkfontein, probably belongs to the Upper Villafranchian portion of the Lower Pleistocene.

Morphology The hominid remains recovered from the excavation include a cranium, parts of other crania, a cranio-facial fragment, parts of a number of mandibles, teeth, parts of maxillae, two left ilia, a right ischium and fragments of humerus, radius, clavicle and femur.

SKULL

The best cranium (MLD 37 and MLD 38) (Dart, 1962a) was found split in half in a divided block of Upper Phase I pink breccia. Subsequent search was rewarded by the recovery of the other half. When the specimens were developed from the matrix and restored they were found to constitute the major part of

Fig. 75   The first Australopithecine cranial fragment (MLD 1) from Makapansgat
Courtesy of Professor P. V. Tobias, photographed by A. R. Hughes

the brain-case, the base of the skull and part of the palate. The remainder of the facial skeleton and the frontal region is missing. The cranium has a remarkable resemblance to the best Sterkfontein skull (Plesianthropus 5) (*q.v.*), only differing in minor respects such as lack of an occipital torus, reduction of the post-glenoid process and in details of the cranial dimensions. The absence of an occipital torus has led to the suggestion that this specimen is probably female. The cranio-facial fragment discloses that the degree of prognathism was not large.   200

MANDIBLES

A range of specimens is available from this site displaying most of the mandibular morphology from infancy to senility. One of the best specimens is half an adult mandible (MLD 40) which contains the canine, premolar and molar teeth. The body of the mandible is stout and on these grounds it is believed to be male. The symphysial region is damaged but the mental foramen is single. The ramus is short by comparison with the large australopithecine from Swartkrans, but comparable with those known from Sterkfontein.

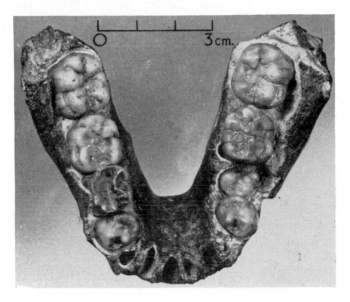

Fig. 76   A juvenile mandible (MLD 2) from Makapansgat
Courtesy of Professor P. V. Tobias, photographed by A. R. Hughes

TEETH

The principal morphological features of the teeth fall within the range of variation of those previously described from Sterkfontein.

POST–CRANIAL BONES

The Ischium (MLD 8) resembles the one that forms part of the Sterkfontein innominate, but differs markedly from the ischia

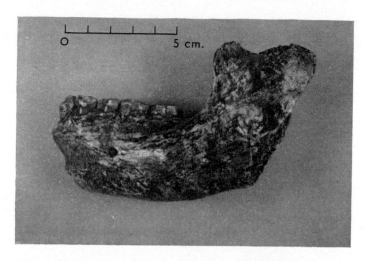

Fig. 77 Half a mandible from Makapansgat
(MLD 40)
Lateral view
*Courtesy of Professor P. V. Tobias,
photographed by A. R. Hughes*

Fig. 78 Half a mandible from Makapansgat
(MLD 40)
Occlusal view
*Courtesy of Professor P. V. Tobias,
photographed by A. R. Hughes*

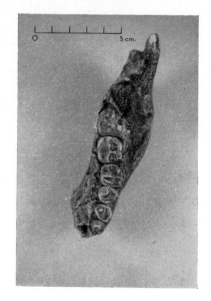

of recent apes and from that of the Swartkrans australo-pithecine. It is a small bone with a moderate ischial tuberosity separated from the remains of the acetabular margin by a groove. This groove is narrower than that shown on the Sterkfontein pelvis and in this respect more nearly resembles the condition found in modern man.

The Ilia are adolescent, small and believed to be of opposite sex, the first specimen male (MLD 7) and the second female (MLD 25). The blade of the ilium is broad and twisted into

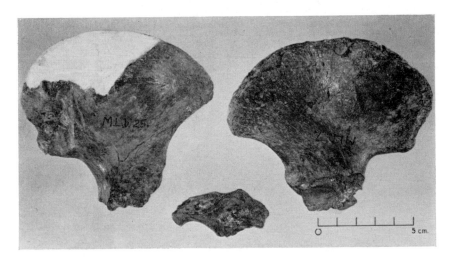

Fig. 79   Two juvenile ilia (MLD 7 and MLD 25) and an ischial fragment (MLD 8) from Makapansgat
Courtesy of Professor P. V. Tobias, photographed by A. R. Hughes

an S-shape when viewed from above. The anterior superior spine is prominent and reaches well forward, recalling the shape of the Swartkrans pelvis. The iliac pillar, which runs upwards from the acetabulum to the tuberosity of the iliac crest, is absent, but some thickening of the cortical bone in this region was disclosed when one specimen was accidently broken.

Although these pelvic fragments differ in a number of respects from their modern human counterparts they differ even more widely from the pelvic bones of modern apes. It is difficult to escape the conclusion that these australopithecines were habitually erect and bipedal in their form of locomotion.

The shaft of the *Humerus* is robust and well marked by the attachment of muscles. It is not unlike that of modern man (Boné, 1955). The remaining post-cranial bones are fragmentary.

Dimensions SKULL
Dart (1962a)
Max. Cranial Breadth 106
MANDIBLE (MLD 40)
Dart (1962b)
Max. Length 123·5 (damaged)
Body Height (M1) 36·0
Body Thickness (M1) 23·5
Max. Ramus Width 45·5
Max. Ramus Height (coronoid) 62·5
TEETH
Robinson (1956), Dart (1962b)

		Upper Permanent Teeth (Crown Dimensions)						
	I1	I2	C	PM1	PM2	M1	M2	M3
Average l	—	—	—	8·8	9·4	12·5	13·9	—
figures b	—	—	—	12·0	12·6	12·8	15·7	—

MLD 40		Lower Permanent Teeth (Crown Dimensions)						
Left l	—	—	8·3★	10·0	10·0	12·8	15·0	15·0
side b	—	—	9·5★	11·0	14·0	12·3	14·3	14·0

★ Damaged

Affinities The affinities of the Makapansgat remains will be discussed with the rest of the australopithecine material.

Originals The Department of Anatomy, Medical School, University of the Witwatersrand, Johannesburg, Republic of South Africa.

Casts The University Museum, University of Pennsylvania, Philadelphia 4, Pennsylvania, U.S.A. (Cranio-facial fragment, adolescent mandible, ischium, ilia, calvarial and maxillary fragments.)

The Makapansgat Remains

DART, R. A. 1948a
The Makapansgat proto-human *Australopithecus prometheus. Am. J. Phys. Anthrop. 6,* 259-284.

DART, R. A. 1948b
The adolescent mandible of *Australopithecus prometheus. Ibid.,* 6, 391-412.

DART, R. A. 1949a
The cranio-facial fragment of *Australopithecus prometheus. Ibid.,* 7, 187-214.

DART, R. A. 1949b
Innominate fragments of *Australopithecus prometheus. Ibid.,* 7, 301-333.

DART, R. A. 1949c
A second adult palate of *Australopithecus prometheus. Ibid.,* 7, 335-338.

MAYR, E. 1950
Taxonomic categories in fossil hominids. *Cold Spring Harbour Symposia on Quantitative Biology 15,* 109-118.

KING, L. C. 1951
The geology of Makapan and other caves. *Trans. Roy. Soc. S. Afr. 33,* 121-151.

DART, R. A. 1954
The second or adult female mandible of *Australopithecus prometheus. Am. J. Phys. Anthrop. 12,* 313-343.

OAKLEY, K. P. 1954
Dating the australopithecines of Africa. *Ibid., 12,* 9-23.

ROBINSON, J. T. 1954
The genera and species of the *Australopithecinae. Ibid., 12,* 181-200.

BONÉ, E. L., and DART, R. A. 1955
A catalogue of australopithecine fossils found at the Limeworks, Makapansgat. *Ibid., 13,* 621-624.

DART, R. A. 1955
Australopithecus prometheus and *Telanthropus capensis. Ibid., 13,* 67-96.

HOWELL, F. C. 1955
The age of the australopithecines of Southern Africa. *Ibid., 13,* 635-662.

ROBINSON, J. T. 1956
The dentition of the *Australopithecinae. Transv. Mus. Mem. 9,* 1-179.

BRAIN, C. K. 1957
New evidence for the correlation of the Transvaal ape-man bearing cave deposits. *Proc. Third Pan-African Cong. Prehist., Livingstone, 1955.* Ed. J. D. Clark, pp. 143-148. London: Chatto and Windus.

DART, R. A. 1957a
The osteodontokeratic culture of *Australopithecus prometheus. Transv. Mus. Mem. 10,* 1-105.

DART, R. A. 1957b
The second adolescent (female) ilium of *Australopithecus prometheus. J. palaeont. Soc. India 2,* 73-82.

205

EWER, R. F. 1957
Faunal evidence on the dating of the *Australopithecinae. Proc. Third Pan-African Cong. Prehist., Livingstone, 1955.* Ed. J. D. Clark, pp. 135-142. London: Chatto and Windus.

OAKLEY, K. P. 1957
Dating the australopithecines. *Ibid.*, pp. 155-157.

BRAIN, C. K. 1958
The Transvaal ape-man bearing cave deposits. *Transv. Mus. Mem. 11*, 1-125.

DART, R. A. 1958
A further adolescent australopithecine ilium from Makapansgat. *Am. J. Phys. Anthrop. 16*, 473-480.

DART, R. A. 1959
The first australopithecine cranium from the pink breccia at Makapansgat. *Ibid.*, *17*, 77-82.

DART, R. A. 1962a
The Makapansgat pink breccia australopithecine skull. *Ibid.*, *20*, 119-126.

DART, R. A. 1962b
A cleft adult mandible and nine other lower jaw fragments from Makapansgat. *Ibid.*, *20*, 267-286.

KURTÉN, B. 1962
The relative ages of the australopithecines of Transvaal and the pithecanthropines of Java. In *Evolution und Hominisation*. Ed. G. Kurth, pp. 74-80. Stuttgart: Gustav Fischer Verlag.

COOKE, H. B. S. 1964
Pleistocene mammal faunas of Africa, with particular reference to South Africa. In *African ecology and human evolution*. Eds. F. C. Howell and F. Bourlière, pp. 65-116. London: Methuen and Co. Ltd.

The announcement of the discovery of the Taung skull by Professor R. A. Dart in 1925, and the creation of a new genus in which to place it, provoked widespread controversy because he firmly emphasized the hominid features of the skull and dentition. Those opposed to Dart's assessment regarded these hominid features as being due to parallel evolution and of little significance. The principal grounds for doubt were reinforced by the fact that the specimen was juvenile. Such a small cranial capacity and such ape-like facial features, in an infant, would indicate a small adult brain size and grossly anthropoid facial features on pedomorphic grounds. None the less, the presence of a first permanent molar of undoubted hominid form should, in retrospect, have cautioned Dart's opponents.

Between 1936 and 1949, Dr Robert Broom, who had supported Dart's opinion, discovered three sites in the Transvaal —Sterkfontein, Kromdraai and Swartkrans—from which, with the assistance of Dr J. T. Robinson, he recovered a great deal of material including skulls, several hundreds of teeth and a number of post-cranial bones. Following Broom's death in 1951, more material was recovered by Robinson. Meanwhile farther north at Makapansgat, Dart was obtaining many new specimens of the same type from similar deposits.

Following the study of these remains it has become clear that the material can be divided into two principal groups, leaving aside for the moment the *Telanthropus* finds from Swartkrans. These groups comprise the remains of a small, generalized, light-framed form represented from Taung, Sterkfontein and Makapansgat, and the remains of a larger, more dentally specialized, robust creature from Kromdraai and Swartkrans. The smaller form seems to be derived from deposits which are earlier than those containing the larger form.

The species represented by the Taung infant skull was named *Australopithecus africanus;* later discoveries of the smaller form were named *Plesianthropus transvaalensis* (Sterkfontein) and *Australopithecus prometheus* (Makapansgat).★

★ The trivial name *prometheus* was given because it was mistakenly believed that there was evidence of the use of fire in association with the fossils at Makapansgat.

It is now widely accepted that the remains from Taung, Sterkfontein and Makapansgat belong to one species only, *A. africanus*. There is less agreement over the classification and nomenclature of the larger form. Broom believed that the

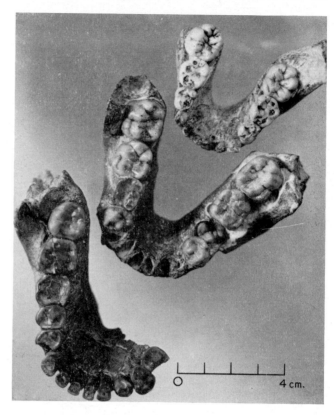

Fig. 80   A series of Australopithecine mandibles
Top—Taung
Middle—Makapansgat juvenile
Bottom—Makapansgat adult
Courtesy of Professor P. V. Tobias, photographed by A. R. Hughes

Kromdraai remains represented a distinct australopithecine genus and named the find *Paranthropus robustus;* later finds from Swartkrans were accepted as congeneric but of a new species *P. crassidens*. Robinson (1954 *et seq.*) has adhered to the

208

generic separation of the larger and smaller forms, accepting *Paranthropus* as a genus containing one species and two subspecies in the Transvaal (*P. robustus robustus* and *P. robustus crassidens*), one species in East Africa (*P. boisei*) and another in the Far East (*P. palaeojavanicus*).

Other authorities regard all of the Transvaal material as representative of one genus containing two species, *Australopithecus africanus* and *Australopithecus robustus* (Oakley, 1954; Campbell, 1964), further distinctions being made between subspecies. Moreover, Mayr (1950) suggested that all the Transvaal material should be included within the genus *Homo*.

There is left the problem of *Telanthropus*. This genus was created by Broom and Robinson on the basis of two crushed mandibles and a premaxillary fragment found at Swartkrans. Following reappraisal this material has been regarded as belonging to the species *Homo erectus*. Until more specimens are available some doubts must remain, but it would seem that the later allocation is probably the right one.

Controversy has surrounded the question of the affinities of the Transvaal australopithecines; the significance of the hominid features of these forms has been strongly advocated by Dart, Broom and Robinson in many publications, a view that has been supported by Le Gros Clark (1947, 1952). This is not to say that the Transvaal australopithecines must have been ancestral to later more advanced hominids such as *Homo erectus* and *Homo sapiens*, indeed it is likely that some of the known individuals from the Transvaal were alive at the same time or soon after early *H. erectus* in Java and thus could not possibly be directly ancestral to this group. No doubt more light will be thrown upon the relationships of all of these early hominids when the East African australopithecine and habiline material has been evaluated. Meanwhile the Transvaal australopithecines provide morphological evidence of a 'prehuman' phase of hominid evolution in which considerable advance had been made in the modification of the teeth for an omnivorous diet, the post-cranial skeleton for the development of upright posture and bipedal gait, whilst expansion of the brain had progressed but little.

209

Additional references   GREGORY, W. K., and HELLMAN, M. 1939
The dentition of the extinct South African man-ape. *Australopithecus (Plesianthropus) transvaalensis* (Broom). *Ann. Transv. Mus.* 19, 339-373.
CLARK, W. E. LE GROS 1952
Hominid characters of the australopithecine dentition. *J. R. anthrop. Inst.* 80, 37-54.
TOBIAS, P. V. 1963
Cranial capacity of *Zinjanthropus* and other australopithecines. *Nature* 197, 743-746.

The Saldanha Skull

Synonyms and other names *Homo saldanensis* (Drennan, 1955); *Homo sapiens rhodesiensis* (Campbell, 1964)
Saldanha man; Hopefield man

Found by K. Jolly and R. Singer, 1953.

Site Elandsfontein Farm, 10 miles south-west of Hopefield and 15 miles south-east of Saldanha Bay, Cape Province, Republic of South Africa.

Geology The remains were found on the surface of sandy veld, 300 feet above sea level. The fossil horizon is made from a nodular calcrete representing a dried-out pan-floor in which the bones had accumulated. Ridges of ferricrete cut across the site and indicated previous wetter conditions, but the fossil layer is capped by surface limestones produced during drought (Mabbutt, 1956 and 1957).

Associated finds The stone tools which were found in great numbers are of three principal types (Singer, 1954; Singer and Crawford 1958).
1. *A Hand-axe Culture* (final Acheulian or Modified Fauresmith). The tools included cleavers, large and pygmy hand-axes, bolas-like stones, pebble choppers and unconventional tools. They were made of silcrete, quartzite, felspar or soft sandstone. The skull bones were associated with this industry.
2. *Middle Stone Age* tools (Stillbay), made of fine-grained ferruginous silcrete.
3. *Later Stone Age* tools, made of felspar and sandstone.
All of these rocks, with the exception of felspar, are foreign to the site.
Supposed bone 'chisels' and 'gouges' reported from the site have been discounted as carnivore chewed and weathered bones (Singer, 1956).
The fossil fauna recovered from the site includes elephant (*cf. Loxodonta atlantica*), a baboon (*Papio ursus*), a large primate (*cf. Simopithecus sp.*), rhinoceros (*cf. Diceros bicornis* and *cf. Ceratotherium simum*), horse (*cf. Equus plicatus*), giant pig (*Mesochoerus lategani*), hippopotamus (*Hippopotamus amphibius*), long-horned buffalo (*Homioceras baini*) and several other artiodactyls and carnivores (Cooke, 1964).

The Saldanha Skull

Dating The geological, archaeological and faunal evidence indicates an early Upper Pleistocene date for these remains. Fluorine and uranium estimations suggest that the skull and the '*Loxodonta-Mesochoerus*' fauna are contemporary.

Morphology Initially 11 fragments were recovered loose on the site, and subsequently more pieces including a portion of mandible. The fragments were fitted together and the cranial vault was finally reconstructed from 27 pieces of bone.

CALVARIUM

The cranial vault is low having a flattened retreating forehead and massive supra-orbital ridges. The parietals are gently rounded but the greatest breadth of the skull must have been near its base. The occipital torus is prominent and the supreme nuchal line is well inscribed; there is no occipital bun-formation. The position of the foramen magnum is not known and the nuchal plane is only partly represented (Singer, 1954). Drennan (1953a and b, 1955) believed that the occipital bone, and thus the nuchal plane, to have been tilted backwards as in the Solo skulls. On these grounds he suggested a crouching posture and a more primitive status for this form, a suggestion dismissed by Singer (1957) as pure conjecture in the absence of most of the occipital bone, the auditory meatus, the orbit and therefore of the Frankfurt Plane orientation.

THE MANDIBLE

The fragment of mandible consists of a portion of the right ramus anterior to the inferior dental canal. Its size and shape indicates that the ramus was broad and the mandibular notch shallow. The fragment is remarkable in its resemblance to the corresponding portion of the Heidelberg jaw.

Dimensions CALVARIUM

Maximum Length 200   Maximum Breadth 144
Cranial Index 72·0 (Dolichocephalic)
Cranial Capacity 1,200–1,250 cc (Drennan, 1953a)
            Calculated 1,250 cc (Drennan, 1953b)

MANDIBULAR FRAGMENT

Alveolar Plane-Coronoid Height 40 (as in the Heidelberg jaw)

Affinities From the beginning the similarity of the Saldanha skull and the Rhodesian skull was recognized, but the morphological identity of the two specimens was not accepted (Drennan, 1953a and b). Where differences occurred the Saldanha skull was said to resemble the Solo skulls, thus Saldanha man was believed to be a more primitive form of Rhodesian man. It was concluded by Singer (1954) that Saldanha and Rhodesian man were African Neanderthalians, unlike the European but similar to the Asiatic representatives of this group, i.e. Solo man. Later Drennan (1955) created a new specific name for Saldanha man, *Homo Saldanensis*; this step was rejected by Singer (1958) who stated that the Saldanha and Rhodesian skulls are similar in the parts that are there to compare, and that their differences are within sex or normal variability limits.

However, it is gradually becoming accepted that both Rhodesian and Saldanha man are of the same subspecies of *Homo sapiens*, *Homo sapiens rhodesiensis* (Campbell, 1964).

Originals South African Museum, Cape Town, Republic of South Africa.

Casts The University Museum, University of Pennsylvania, Philadelphia 4, Pennsylvania, U.S.A. (Calvarium only).

References DRENNAN, M. R. 1953a
A preliminary note on the Saldanha skull. *S. Afr. J. Sci. 50*, 7-11.
DRENNAN, M. R. 1953b
The Saldanha skull and its associations. *Nature 172*, 791-793.
SINGER, R. 1954
The Saldanha skull from Hopefield, South Africa. *Am. J. Phys. Anthrop. 12*, 345-362.
DRENNAN, M. R. 1955
The special features and status of the Saldanha skull. *Am. J. Phys. Anthrop. 13*, 625-634.
DRENNAN, M. R., and SINGER, R. 1955
A mandibular fragment, probably of the Saldanha skull. *Nature 175*, 364-365.
MABBUTT, J. A. 1956
The physiography and surface geology of the Hopefield fossil site. *Trans. roy. Soc. S. Afr. 35*, 21-58.
SINGER, R. 1956
The 'bone tools' from Hopefield. *Amer. Anthrop. 58*, 1127-1134.
MABBUTT, J. A. 1957
The physical background to the Hopefield discoveries. *Proc. Third Pan-African Cong. Prehist.*, *Livingstone, 1955*. Ed. J. D. Clark, pp. 68-75. London: Chatto and Windus.

OAKLEY, K. P. 1957
The dating of the Broken Hill, Florisbad and Saldanha skulls. *Proc. Third Pan-African Con. Prehist., Livingstone, 1955*. Ed. J. D. Clark. pp. 76-79. London: Chatto and Windus.

SINGER, R. 1957
Investigations at the Hopefield site. *Ibid.*, pp. 175-182.

SINGER, R. 1958
The Rhodesian, Florisbad and Saldanha skulls. In *Hundert Jahre Neanderthaler*. Ed. G. H. R. von Koenigswald, pp. 52-62. Utrecht: Kemink en Zoon.

SINGER, R., and CRAWFORD, J. R. 1958
The significance of the archaeological discoveries at Hopefield, South Africa. *J. R. anthrop. Inst. 88*, 11-19.

CAMPBELL, B. 1964
Quantitative taxonomy and human evolution. In *Classification and human evolution*. Ed. S. L. Washburn, pp. 50-74. London: Methuen and Co. Ltd.

The Florisbad Skull

Synonyms and other names	*Homo* (*Africanthropus*) *helmei* (Dreyer, 1935); *Homo florisbadensis* (*helmei*) (Drennan, 1935); *Homo sapiens* (Vallois, 1957)
Found by	T. F. Dreyer, 1932.
Site	Florisbad, 30 miles north of Bloemfontein, Orange Free State, Republic of South Africa.
Geology	The deposits are on the southern slope of the Hagenstad salt-pan which is near a medicinal watering place. The area is marked by numerous springs, many of which have become choked with accumulated debris; when this occurs a new spring eye opens near by. The debris consists of sand containing stone artefacts, broken bones and teeth. The heavier sand is ilmenite with garnets and diopside, whilst above this layer there is a cap of pure white quartz sand (Dreyer, 1935).
	Recent investigation of the site has disclosed a profile of eleven strata including a basal layer and four other layers of 'peat'. These 'peat' layers are in fact dark coloured sand and clay containing little organic matter.
	The skull was found at the side of the eye of a spring beneath the 'Peat I' stratum about 18 feet from the surface.
Associated finds	Dreyer reported the occurrence of stone tools of African Middle Stone Age culture. In particular one group of Mousterian-like blades known as the Hagenstad variation was recovered from the deeper layers.
	The fossil mammalian fauna that was found includes several living rodents and carnivores as well as extinct species such as giant buffalo (*Connochaetes antiquus*, *Alcelaphus helmei*) and two equids (*Equus helmei*, *Equus burchelli*) (Cooke, 1964).
Dating	The stratigraphy of this specimen is confusing from the point of view of establishing its age. However, the implements suggest that the deposits belong to the Upper Pleistocene or even the Holocene. A pollen investigation (van Zinderen Bakker, 1957) suggests that the oldest parts of the profile were probably formed at the beginning of the Upper Pleistocene during a dry phase or interpluvial. The radiocarbon dates of 41,000 years B.P. given for the 'Dark Layer I' by Libby (1954)

215

and of 37,000 years B.P. (quoted by van Zinderen Bakker, 1957) have been considered too high because the Pleistocene plant material in that layer is probably contaminated by 'dead carbon' carried up by the spring from underlying Palaeozoic coal measures (Oakley, 1957).

Morphology The skull fragment consists of part of the face and vault including the right orbital margin and part of the maxilla; the base of the skull and the mandible are missing.

The cranium is large but rather flattened with no parietal, and feeble frontal, bosses. The superciliary ridges are as those found in modern man, there being no evidence of a supra-orbital torus. The face is moderately prognathic. The palate is incomplete and the only tooth present is the right upper third molar which is very worn.

Dimensions Max. Length approx. 200   Max. Breadth approx. 150.

Affinities In the original description of this skull Dreyer (1935) named the specimen *Homo (Africanthropus) helmei* thus asserting that this form was sub-generically distinct from other members of the genus *Homo*. However, in the same publication Kappers, who had studied the endocranial cast, emphasized its likeness to *Homo sapiens fossilis*. Drennan (1935, 1937) urged the Neanderthal characters of this skull and endocast on metrical grounds, and proposed the name *Homo florisbadensis (helmei)* as being more appropriate. This view was opposed by Galloway (1937, 1938) who emphasized that the non-metrical features of the Florisbad skull linked it with *Homo sapiens*, and moreover with the Australoid variety of this species. Similarly Boule and Vallois (1957) unequivocally classified these remains as belonging to *Homo sapiens*.

Original National Museum, Bloemfontein, Orange Free State, Republic of South Africa.

Casts The University Museum, University of Pennsylvania, Philadelphia 4, Pennsylvania, U.S.A.

References DREYER, T. F. 1935
A human skull from Florisbad. *Proc. Acad. Sci. Amst. 38*, 119-128.
DRENNAN, M. R. 1935
The Florisbad skull. *S. Afr. J. Sci. 32.* 601-602.
DREYER, T. F. 1936
The endocranial cast of the Florisbad skull—a correction. *Sool. Nav. nas. Mus. Bloemfontein 1*, 21-23.

DRENNAN, M. R. 1937
The Florisbad skull and brain cast. *Trans. roy. Soc. S. Afr. 25*, 103-114.

GALLOWAY, A. 1937
Man in Africa in the light of recent discoveries. *S. Afr. J. Sci. 34*, 89-120.

GALLOWAY, A. 1938
The nature and status of the Florisbad skull as revealed by its non-metrical features. *Am. J. Phys. Anthrop. 23*, 1-16.

LIBBY, W. F. 1954
Chicago radiocarbon dates, V. *Science 120*, 733-742.

BAKKER, E. M. VAN ZINDEREN 1957
A pollen analytical investigation of the Florisbad deposits (South Africa). *Proc. Third Pan-African Cong. Prehist., Livingstone, 1955*. Ed. J. D. Clark, pp. 56-57. London: Chatto and Windus.

OAKLEY, K. P. 1957
The dating of the Broken Hill, Florisbad and Saldanha skulls. *Ibid.*, pp. 76-79.

BOULE, M., and VALLOIS, H. V. 1957
Fossil man, 4th Ed., p. 462. London: Thames and Hudson.

SINGER, R. 1958
The Rhodesian, Florisbad and Saldanha skulls. In *Hundert Jahre Neanderthaler*. Ed. G. H. R. von Koenigswald, pp. 52-62. Utrecht: Kemink en Zoon.

COOKE, H. B. S. 1964
Pleistocene mammal faunas of Africa, with particular reference to Southern Africa. In *African ecology and human evolution*. Eds. F. C. Howell and F. Bourlière, pp. 65-116. London: Methuen and Co. Ltd.

The Far East

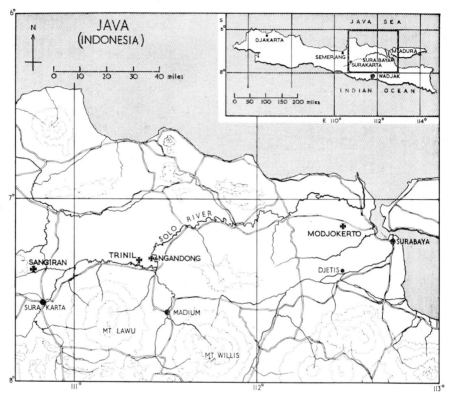

Fig. 81 Hominid fossil sites in Java

The Trinil Calotte and Femur

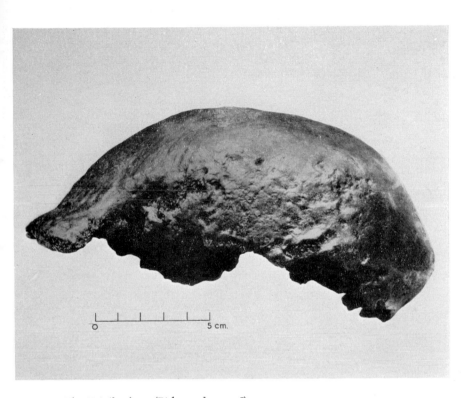

Fig. 82   The Trinil calotte (Pithecanthropus I)
          Left lateral view
          Courtesy of Professor J. S. Weiner and Dr D. A. Hooijer

Synonyms   *Pithecanthropus erectus* (Dubois, 1894); Pithecanthropus I
and other names   (von Koenigswald and Weidenreich, 1939); *Homo erectus
javensis* (Weidenreich, 1940); *Homo erectus* (Mayr, 1950);
Homo erectus erectus (Dobzhansky, 1944; Campbell, 1964)
Java man

Site   Trinil, approximately 20 miles north-west of Madium, six
miles west of Ngawi, Central Java, Indonesia.

Found by   Eugene Dubois, 1891.

Geology   Trinil lies at the foot of a volcano, Lawu, whose lavas and
cinders have spilled over a wide area. Elevated Pleistocene   221

deposits include the Solo beds which have been subdivided into the Djetis, the Trinil and the later Ngandong strata. The calotte was found in the Trinil layer, which consists of fresh-water sandstones and conglomerates containing volcanic material, within a few yards of the waters of the river Solo. The femur was uncovered 15 metres upstream.

Associated finds No artefacts were found in association with the remains, but numerous fossil mammalian bones have been recovered from the site. Amongst these were the remains of stegodont elephant (*Stegodon*), rhinoceros (*Rhinoceros sondaicus*), carnivores (*Felis*), and some ungulates including axis deer (*Axis leydekkeri*) and a small antelope (*Duboisia kroesenii*) (Selenka and Blancken-horn, 1911).

Dating According to von Koenigswald (1934, 1949), three series of deposits succeeded each other in Central Java; the Djetis (Lower Pleistocene), the Trinil (Mid-Pleistocene) and the Ngandong (Upper Pleistocene) with a more recent fauna. Hooijer (1951, 1956, 1957, 1962) has accepted the Trinil bed as Mid-Pleistocene, but has denied a faunal distinction between the Djetis and Trinil layers and claims that they are probably both Middle Pleistocene. Estimations of the fluorine content of the Trinil calotte and femur have established their contemporaneity both with each other and with their associated fauna (Bergman and Karsten, 1952). In an attempt to correlate the dating of European, African and Asian fossils Kurtén (1962) has equated *Pithecanthropus erectus* of Java with *Paranthropus* from South Africa, and assigned to them both a Middle Pleistocene date (Mindel or Antepenultimate Glaciation). Finally by the use of the radiometric potassium–argon dating method of tektites and basalt found in deposits which are said to correspond with those at Trinil, von Koenigswald *et al.* (1962) have claimed a chronological age of 550,000 years B.P. for *Pithecanthropus erectus*, within the First Glaciation (Günz or Early Glaciation).

Morphology The calotte is made up of parts of the frontal, parietal and occipital bones with little or no sign of suture lines. It is thick, undistorted and heavily mineralized. The frontal region of the vault is markedly flattened in profile, leading forwards to a heavy supra-orbital torus which is hollowed by paired frontal air sinuses. Behind the brow ridge the frontal region is sharply constricted producing a post-orbital waist, whilst in the midline the bone is heaped into a sessile ridge or keel. The temporal lines are well shown but widely separated. Internally the calotte is moulded by the cerebral convolutions and grooved by the meningeal blood vessels.

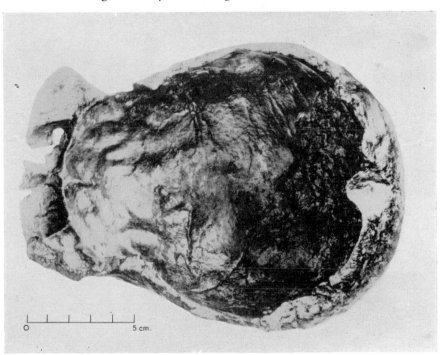

5 cm.

Fig. 83   The Trinil calotte (Pithecanthropus I)
Internal view
Courtesy of Professor J. S. Weiner and Dr D. A. Hooijer

The femur is remarkable in its general resemblance to that of modern man. The shaft is straight and has a prominent linea aspera, but in its upper third the specimen is marred by a pathological outgrowth. The head of the bone is rounded, the neck stout and angulated to the shaft, whilst the greater and lesser trochanters are well developed indicating the attachment of powerful muscles around the hip joint.

The features of this femur, in particular the 'weight-carrying-angle' between the shaft and the condyles, suggest strongly   223 that Java man was capable of standing and walking erectly. More precise evaluation of the stance and gait of this form must await the discovery of more material, in particular the bones of the pelvis and foot.

Dimensions CALOTTE

Length 183   Breadth 134

Cephalic Index 70 (Dolichocephalic)

Cranial capacity 900 cc (Dubois, 1924)

> 914 cc (von Koenigswald and Weidenreich, 1939)
>
> 850 cc (Boule and Vallois, 1957)
>
> 940 cc (Ashley Montagu, 1960)

FEMUR (Taken from cast)

Length 455   Mean mid-shaft diameter 28

Bicondylar breadth 77   Mean diameter of head 44

Angle of neck 125°   Femoro-condylar angle 100°

Affinities These were the first significant finds in the search for fossil man in the Far East. Despite the opposition of Dubois, subsequent finds at Sangiran and Modjokerto (*q.v.*) confirmed that the Trinil specimens are representative of a group of hominids who occupied Java in the Middle Pleistocene. Further finds in China (Peking man) suggested that hominds of this grade were widely distributed in the Far East, for the morphological differences between the two groups indicate only racial variation (Weidenreich, 1938, 1940). Recently Java man has been classified as *Homo erectus erectus*, only subspecifically distinct from *Homo erectus pekinensis* (Dobzhansky, 1944; Campbell, 1964).

Originals Collection Dubois, Rijksmuseum von Natuurlijke Historie, Leiden, Netherlands.

Casts 1. Rijksmuseum von Natuurlijke Historie, Leiden, Netherlands.

2. The University Museum, University of Pennsylvania, Philadelphia 4, Pennsylvania U.S.A.

References DUBOIS, E. 1894
Pithecanthropus erectus, *eine menschenaehnliche Ubergangsform aus Java.* Batavia: Landesdruckerei.
SELENKA, M. L., and BLANCKENHORN, M. 1911
Die Pithecanthropus—*Schichten auf Java.* Leipzig: Verlag von Wilhelm Engelmann.

DUBOIS, E. 1924
On the principal characters of the cranium and the brain, the mandible and the teeth of *Pithecanthropus erectus*. *Proc. Acad. Sci. Amst. 27,* 265-278.

DUBOIS, E. 1926
On the principal characters of the femur of *Pithecanthropus erectus*. *Proc. Acad. Sci. Amst. 29,* 730-743.

WEINERT, H. 1928
Pithecanthropus erectus. *Z. ges. Anat. 87,* 429-547.

KOENIGSWALD, G. H. R. VON 1934
Zur Stratigraphie des javanischen Pleistocän. *Ing. Ned. Ind. 1,* 185-201.

WEIDENREICH, F. 1938
Pithecanthropus and *Sinanthropus*. *Nature 141,* 378-379.

WEIDENREICH, F. 1940
Some problems dealing with ancient man. *Amer. Anthrop. 42,* 375-383.

DOBZHANSKY, T. 1944
On the species and races of living and fossil men. *Am. J. Phys. Anthrop. 2,* 251-265.

KOENIGSWALD, G. H. R. VON, 1949
The discovery of early man in Java and Southern China. In *Early man in the Far East.* Ed. W. W. Howells; Philadelphia. *Stud. Phys. Anthrop. 1,* 83-98.

MAYR, E. 1950
Taxonomic categories in fossil hominids. *Cold Spring Harbour Symposia on Quantitative Biology 15,* 109-118.

HOOIJER, D. A. 1951
The geological age of *Pithecanthropus, Meganthropus* and *Gigantopithecus. Am. J. Phys. Anthrop. 9,* 265-281.

BERGMAN, R. A. M., and KARSTEN, P. 1952
The fluorine content of *Pithecanthropus* and other specimens from the Trinil fauna. *Proc. Acad. Sci. Amst. B. 55,* 1, 150-152.

HOOIJER, D. A. 1956
The lower boundary of the Pleistocene in Java and the age of *Pithecanthropus. Quarternaria 3,* 1, 5-10.

HOOIJER, D. A. 1957
The correlation of fossil mammalian faunas and the Plio-Pleistocene boundary in Java. *Proc. Acad. Sci. Amst. B. 60,* 1-10.

HOOIJER, D. A. 1962
The Middle Pleistocene fauna of Java. In *Evolution und Hominisation.* Ed. G. Kurth. pp. 108-111. Stuttgart: Gustav Fischer Verlag.

KURTÉN, B. 1962
The australopithecines of Transvaal and the pithecanthropines of Java. *Ibid.,* pp. 74-80.

KOENIGSWALD, G. H. R. VON 1962
Das absolute Alter des *Pithecanthropus erectus* Dubois. *Ibid.,* pp. 112-119.

The First Sangiran Calvarium

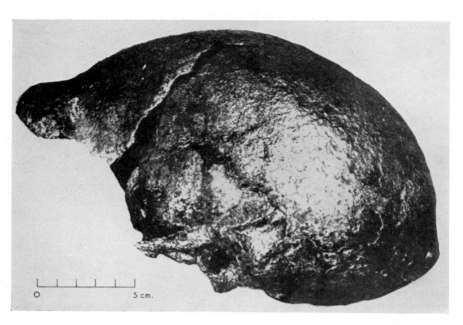

Fig. 84   The first Sangiran calvarium (Pithecanthropus II)
Left lateral view
Courtesy of Professor J. S. Weiner

Synonyms and other names   *Pithecanthropus* (von Koenigswald, 1938); Pithecanthropus II (von Koenigswald and Weidenreich, 1939); *Homo erectus* (Mayr, 1950); *Homo erectus erectus* (Campbell, 1964)

Site   Sangiran, by the river Tjemoro, a tributary of the Solo, about 40 miles west of Trinil near Surakarta, Central Java, Indonesia.

Found by   G. H. R. von Koenigswald, September, 1937.

Geology   The calvarium was found in a sedimentary Pleistocene stratum consisting of river sandstone, conglomerates and volcanic tufas, which corresponds with the layer that contained the Trinil calotte and femur (Trinil deposits).

Associated finds   No artefacts were associated with the find, but the fossil fauna equates with that found at Trinil (*q.v.*).

Dating   On both stratigraphic and faunal grounds the dating of this

226

find is approximately the same as that of the Trinil remains (*q.v.*), probably early Mid-Pleistocene. However, potassium–argon dating of basalt and tektites from similar Trinil deposits (von Koenigswald, 1962) has indicated an age of 550,000 years B.P. for *Pithecanthropus erectus*, probably during the European First Glaciation (Günz or Early Glaciation).

Morphology The calvarium consists of the frontal, parietal, temporal and occipital bones of an adult; both facial skeleton and skull base are missing. The region of the foramen magnum and the right side of the frontal bone are broken away. In general form the specimen strongly resembles the Trinil calotte; the flattening and keeling of the frontal region, the supra-orbital torus and the widely separated temporal lines are features common to both. The occipital bone of the Sangiran calvarium shows that the nuchal plane is inclined at an angle intermediate between that of the pongids and modern man; the supra-mastoid and occipital crests are in continuity and the mastoid processes are very small. The position of the foramen magnum is placed forward, evidence that *Pithecanthropus* was habitually upright in posture. Internally the bones are impressed by the cerebral convolutions and grooved by the larger dural venous sinuses and meningeal vessels.

Dimensions Length *c.* 180   Max. Breadth 140
Cephalic Index 77·8 (Mesocephalic)
Cranial Capacity   *c.* 750 cc (von Koenigswald, 1938)
                 850 cc (Weidenreich, 1938)
                 775 cc (von Koenigswald, 1949)
                 815 cc (Boule and Vallois, 1957)
Comparison of the dimensions of the Sangiran calvarium with those of the Trinil calotte led to the suggestion that the Sangiran specimen was female (von Koenigswald, 1938).

Affinities There is little doubt that the Sangiran calvarium belonged to a hominid of the same type as that of the Trinil calotte; in consequence it was attributed to *Pithecanthropus* by von Koenigswald (1938) and considered only racially distinct from Peking man (von Koenigswald and Weidenreich, 1939). This view was strongly contested by Dubois (1940) who alleged that this skull was really the remains of a Solo man (*Homo soloensis*), said to be synonymous with Wadjak man (*Homo*

227

wadjakensis). Despite this controversy it was apparent that Pithecanthropus I and II were almost identical. Subsequently both the Trinil and Sangiran forms have been recognized as members of the genus *Homo* (*Homo erectus*) (Mayr, 1950). Recently the Javan representatives of *Homo erectus* have been classified separately as *Homo erectus erectus*, only subspecifically distinct from Peking and possibly from Ternifine man (Campbell, 1964).

Originals   G. H. R. von Koenigswald Collection, Geologisch Instituut, Der Rijksuniversiteit te Utrecht, Utrecht, Netherlands.

Casts   The University Museum, University of Pennsylvania, Philadelphia 4, Pennsylvania, U.S.A.

References   KOENIGSWALD, G. H. R. VON 1938
Ein neuer *Pithecanthropus*-Schädel *Proc. Acad. Sci. Amst. 41*, 185-192.
KOENIGSWALD, G. H. R. VON, and WEIDENREICH, F. 1939
The relationship between *Pithecanthropus* and *Sinanthropus*. *Nature 144*, 926-929.
DUBOIS, E. 1940
The fossil human remains discovered in Java by Dr. G. H. R. von Koenigswald and attributed by him to *Pithecanthropus erectus*, in reality remains of *Homo wadjakensis* (syn. *Homo soloensis*). *Proc. Acad. Sci. Amst. 43*, 494-496, 842-851, 1268-1275.
WEIDENREICH, F. 1945
The puzzle of *Pithecanthropus*. *Science and scientists in the Netherlands Indies*. New York: Board for the Netherlands Indies, Surinam and Curaçao.
KOENIGSWALD, G. H. R. VON 1949
The discovery of early man in Java and Southern China. In *Early man in the Far East*. Ed. W. W. Howells: Philadelphia. *Stud. Phys. Anthrop. 1*, 83-98.
MAYR, E. 1950
Taxonomic categories in fossil hominids. *Cold Spring Harbour Symposia on Quantitative Biology 15*, 109-118.
KOENIGSWALD, G. H. R. VON 1962
Das absolute Alter des *Pithecanthropus erectus* Dubois. In *Evolution und Hominisation*. Ed. G. Kurth, pp. 112-119. Stuttgart: Gustav Fischer Verlag.
CAMPBELL, B. 1964
Quantitative taxonomy and human evolution. In *Classification and human evolution*. Ed. S. L. Washburn, pp. 50-74. London: Methuen and Co. Ltd.

228

The Second Sangiran Calvarium and Maxillae

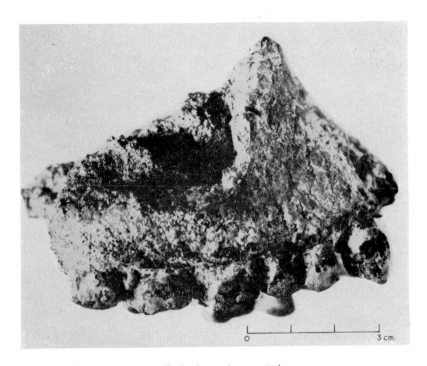

Fig. 85   The Sangiran maxilla (Pithecanthropus IV)
Right lateral view
Courtesy of Professor G. H. R. von Koenigswald

Synonyms Pithecanthropus IV (von Koenigswald and Weidenreich,
and other names 1939); *Pithecanthropus* (von Koenigswald, 1942); *Pithecan-*
thropus robustus (Weidenreich, 1945); *Pithecanthropus modjoker-*
tensis (von Koenigswald, 1950); *Homo erectus* (Mayr, 1950);
Pithecanthropus erectus (Piveteau, 1957); *Homo erectus erectus*
(Dobzhansky, 1944, Campbell, 1964)

Site Sangiran, by the river Tjemoro, a tributary of the Solo, about
40 miles west of Trinil, near Surakarta, Central Java, Indonesia.

Found by Collectors employed by G. H. R. von Koenigswald, January,
1939.

Geology The remains were found in the Djetis layer that underlies the
Trinil deposits at Sangiran.

229

Associated finds No artefacts were recovered with the specimens. The fossil mammalian fauna known from the Djetis beds in this region includes a primitive horned ox (*Leptobos*) and a sabre-toothed cat (*Epimachairodus*).

Dating At first the stratigraphy and the fauna contained in the Djetis beds at Sangiran suggested a Lower Pleistocene date for these remains (von Koenigswald, 1934, 1949). However, more recently von Koenigswald has argued for a Villafranchian date within the Lower Pleistocene for the Djetis beds (von Koenigswald, 1956). Both views have been strongly contested by Hooijer (1951, 1956, 1957, 1962) who equates the Trinil and Djetis beds on faunal grounds and places the deposits in the early post-Villafranchian portion of the Middle Pleistocene. Potassium-argon dating (von Koenigswald, 1962) of basalt and tekites from Trinil layers suggests an age for these deposits of 550,000 B.P., probably during the European First Glaciation (Günz or Early Glaciation). If this is proved correct it would lend weight to von Koenigswald's assessment of the age of the underlying Djetis beds.

Morphology The remains consist of the posterior half of a brain case and the lower portion of both maxillae.

CALVARIUM

The cranium is represented by almost the entire occipital bone, including the foramen magnum and the occipital condyles, the temporal bones and approximately the posterior three-quarters of both parietal bones. The skull is larger than that of Pithecanthropus I or II, but resembles them in that it has a low vault and has its greatest breadth at the base. There is a marked frontal keel accentuated by parasagittal depressions and a series of 'knob-like' processes leading back from the vertex to the occipital torus—features not seen in any other pithecanthropine. The occipital torus is very large and joins the supra-mastoid ridges on either side; the nuchal muscles have left well marked impressions on the occipital bone indicating a powerful neck. The mastoid processes are large and project downwards and inwards, in contrast to the small processes of the first Sangiran calvarium. The external auditory meatus is oval as in modern man but the tympanic plate is thick; the mandibular fossa is deep and narrow and the articular eminence is absent. Internally the petrous temporal bone is very prominent.

THE MAXILLAE

The alveolar processes are complete except for the posterior part of the left side. In addition almost the entire palate, the floor of the nasal cavity and the maxillary sinuses of both sides are preserved.

The maxillae were crushed before fossilization, resulting in some distortion. The bony palate is very large and smooth, relieved only by the presence of the palatal groove on the right side which is limited medially by an unusual bony prominence. The incisive canal is double and has a funnel–like opening which is very large and distally placed. The pre-maxillary region is very deep but the pillars of the zygomatic bones arise near the alveolar borders. In lateral view the degree of facial and alveolar prognathism is large but there is no typical nasal spine. The maxillary sinus is large but does not extend back into the maxillary tuberosity.

THE TEETH

All the teeth are present except the incisors and the left second and third molars. An isolated incisor was found with the previous specimens. The teeth are very little worn. The incisor sockets indicate that the teeth sloped forwards, and that a wide diastema existed between the lateral incisor and the canine. The canines are large by comparison with hominid teeth and their breadths exceed their lengths. The molars decrease in size in the order $M_2 > M_1 > M_3$, and the cusp pattern of their crowns does not differ appreciably from those of Peking man except that the remains of the cingulum are less obvious in the Sangiran molars.

Dimensions   *Weidenreich* (1945)

CALVARIUM

Max. Length 199   Max. Breadth ? 158
Cranial Index ? 79·3   Cranial Capacity *c.* 900 cc

			Upper Teeth (Crown Dimensions)						
Pith. IV		I_1	I_2	C	PM_1	PM_2	M_1	M_2	M_3
Left	l	—	—	9·5	8·5	8·5	12·3	—	—
	b	—	—	11·9	12·4	12·3	13·6	—	—
Right	l	—	10·0	9·5	8·2	8·2	12·1	13·6	10·8
	b	—	10·4	11·7	12·4	12·1	13·7	15·2	14·0

231

Affinities The remains were examined and described by Weidenreich (1945) and a tentative reconstruction of the skull was attempted. At first he believed that this calvarium was male and therefore that the previously known specimens must be female. However, he later abandoned this idea as he could not reconcile some of the features of the skull with this scheme of interpretation and assumed that it must belong to a separate group, *Pithecanthropus robustus*. Von Koenigswald (1950) could not accept this view and allied Pithecanthropus IV with a mandibular fragment from Sangiran known as Pithecanthropus B, and named them both *Pithecanthropus modjokertensis*. Subsequently it has become clear that Pithecanthropus IV is closely allied to the other pithecanthropines of the Far East and in particular those of Java, *Homo erectus erectus* (Dobzhansky, 1944; Campbell, 1964).

A recent comparison of the Pithecanthropus IV maxillae with the right maxilla of the Lower Bed II hominine from Olduvai (Olduvai Hominid 13) and a similar comparison of the Pithecanthropus B mandibular fragment with the Hominid 13 mandible has revealed remarkable similarities (Tobias and von Koenigswald, 1964). Although it is early to assess the significance of these findings it appears that the later forms of *Homo habilis* may be equivalent in grade of hominization to the early forms of *Pithecanthropus* in Java.

Originals G. H. R. von Koenigswald Collection, Geologisch Instituut, Der Rijksuniversiteit te Utrecht, Utrecht, Netherlands.

Casts Not available at present.

References KOENIGSWALD, G. H. R. VON 1934
Zur Stratigraphie des javanischen Pleistocän. *Ing. Ned. Ind. 1, 4,* 185-201.
KOENIGSWALD, G. H. R. VON, and WEIDENREICH, F. 1939
The relationship between *Pithecanthropus* and *Sinanthropus*. *Nature 144,* 926-929.
KOENIGSWALD, G. H. R. VON 1942
The South African man-apes and *Pithecanthropus*. *Carnegie Inst. Washington. Publ. No. 530,* pp. 205-222.
DOBZHANSKY, T. 1944
On species and races of living and fossil men. *Am. J. Phys. Anthrop. 2,* 251-265.
WEIDENREICH, F. 1945
Giant early-man from Java and South China. *Anthrop. Pap. Amer. Mus. 40,* 1-134.

KOENIGSWALD, G. H. R. VON, 1949
The discovery of early man in Java and Southern China. In *Early man in the Far East*. Ed. W. W. Howells, Philadelphia. *Stud. Phys. Anthrop. 1*, 83-98.

KOENIGSWALD, G. H. R. VON 1950
Fossil hominids from the Lower Pleistocene of Java. *Proc. Ninth Internat. Geol. Cong., London, 1948. Sect. 9*, pp. 59-61.

MAYR, E. 1950
Taxonomic categories in fossil hominids. *Cold Spring Harbour Symposia on Quantitative Biology 15*, 109-118.

HOOIJER, D. A. 1951
The geological age of *Pithecanthropus, Meganthropus* and *Gigantopithecus. Am. J. Phys. Anthrop. 9*, 265-281.

HOOIJER, D. A. 1956
The lower boundary of the Pleistocene in Java and the age of *Pithecanthropus. Quarternaria 3*, 5-10.

KOENIGSWALD, G. H. R. VON 1956
Remarks on the correlation of mammalian faunas of Java, India and the Plio-Pleistocene boundary. *Proc. Acad. Sci. Amst. B. 59*, 204-210.

HOOIJER, D. A. 1957
The correlation of fossil mammalian faunas and the Plio-Pleistocene in Java. *Proc. Acad. Sci. Amst. B. 60*, 1-10.

PIVETEAU, J. 1957
Traité de Paléontologie VII. Paris: Masson et Cie.

HOOIJER, D. A. 1962
The Middle Pleistocene fauna of Java. In *Evolution und Hominisation*. Ed. G. Kurth, pp. 108-111. Stuttgart: Gustav Fischer Verlag.

KOENIGSWALD, G. H. R. VON 1962
Das absolute Alter des *Pithecanthropus erectus* Dubois. *Ibid.*, pp. 112-119.

CAMPBELL, B. 1964
Quantitative taxonomy and human evolution. In *Classification and human evolution*. Ed. S. L. Washburn, pp. 50-74. London: Methuen and Co. Ltd.

TOBIAS, P. V., and KOENIGSWALD, G. H. R. VON, 1964
A comparison between the Olduvai hominines and those of Java and some implications for hominid phylogeny. *Nature, 204*, 515-518.

The Modjokerto Infant Calvarium

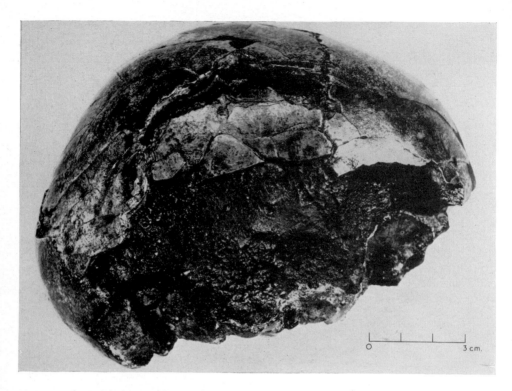

Fig. 86   The Modjokerto infant calvarium
            Right lateral view
            Courtesy of Professor G. H. R. von Koenigswald

Synonyms and other names	*Homo modjokertensis* (von Koenigswald, 1936a); *Homo solensis* (Dubois, 1936); *Pithecanthropus modjokertensis* (von Koenigswald, 1950); *Homo erectus* (Mayr, 1950); *Homo erectus erectus* (Campbell, 1964)
Site	Modjokerto, 18 miles west-north-west of Surabaya, Java, Indonesia.
Found by	J. Duyfjes, 1936.
Geology	The calvarium was discovered in a bed of Pleistocene river sands and marine sediments named the Djetis, situated at a lower stratigraphic level than that which contained the Trinil remains (*q.v.*).

234

Associated finds   No artefacts were recovered with the specimen but the fossil fauna included primitive ox (*Leptobos*), sabre-toothed cat (*Epimachairodus*) and a small Rusa deer (*Cervus zwaani*); forms typical of the Djetis.

Dating   It has been held that the stratigraphy and the fauna associated with the find suggest that the Djetis beds were laid down before the Trinil beds in Java; on this account they were attributed to the Lower Pleistocene by von Koenigswald (1934, 1949). Later, von Koenigswald has argued for a Villa-franchian date for the Djetis (1956). The Lower Pleistocene age of this layer has been contested by Hooijer (1951, 1956, 1957, 1962) who believes both the Djetis and the Trinil beds to be of Middle Pleistocene age. Kurtén (1962) states that *Pithecanthropus modjokertensis* from the Djetis is probably of First or Cromerian Interglacial (Günz–Mindel or Antepenultimate Interglacial) age and thus the same as *Australopithecus africanus*. Potassium–argon dating of basalt and tektites from deposits comparable with the Javan Trinil layer has indicated an age of approximately 500,000–600,000 years B.P., an age which tends to support the contention that the underlying Djetis is even older.

Morphology   The calvarium consists of the frontal, parietal, temporal and occipital bones of an infant, and lacks part of the base and the entire facial skeleton. The bones of the vault are thin and the anterior fontanelle had probably only just closed at the time of death. The mandibular fossa is deep and the articular eminence pronounced. In general outline the vault narrows anteriorly producing some post-orbital constriction and lateral flaring of the orbital margin. The recession of the forehead is more marked than that of a modern child of equivalent age, whilst the occiput shows no sign of a torus. The age at death has been estimated as two years (Dubois, 1936) but von Koenigswald (1936b) declined to make an estimation.

Dimensions   Max. Length 138   Max. Breadth 110
Cephalic Index 83·4
Cranial capacity ≏2–3 year European child (von Koenigswald, 1963b).
Cranial capacity 650 cc (Dubois, 1936).
Cranial capacity 700 cc (Boule and Vallois, 1957)

The Modjokerto Infant Calvarium

Affinities At first von Koenigswald (1936a) avoided naming this find *Pithecanthropus*, in deference to Dubois, and termed it *Homo modjokertensis;* Dubois (1936), supported initially by Weidenreich (1938), believed it to be an infant *Homo soloensis*. Subsequently, after examining the original, Weidenreich accepted that it was a baby *Pithecanthropus* (von Koenigswald and Weidenreich, 1939).

Grimm (1940) took the view that the Modjokerto infant was neanderthaloid yet resembled Peking man. However, more recently von Koenigswald (1950) has underlined the resemblance of this calvarium to the other pithecanthropines and renamed the specimen *Pithecanthropus modjokertensis*. It has followed that this specimen, with the other Javan pithecanthropines, has been classified first as a member of the genus *Homo* (*H. erectus*) (Mayr, 1950) but later as probably only subspecifically distinct from Peking and Ternifine man (Campbell, 1964).

Originals G. H. R. von Koenigswald Collection, Geologisch Institute, Der Rijksuniversiteit te Utrecht, Utrecht, Netherlands.

Casts The University Museum, University of Pennsylvania, Philadelphia 4, Pennsylvania, U.S.A.

References KOENIGSWALD, G. H. R. VON 1934
Zur Stratigraphie des javanischen Pleistocän. *Ing. Ned. Ind. 1*, 185–201.
KOENIGSWALD, G. H. R. VON 1936a
Erste Mitteilung über einen fossilen Hominiden aus dem Altpleistocän Ostjavas. *Proc. Acad. Sci. Amst. 39*, 1000–1009.
KOENIGSWALD, G. H. R. VON 1936b
Ein fossiler Hominide aus dem Altpeistocän Ostjavas. *Ing. Ned. Ind. 3*, 149–157.
DUYFJES, J. 1936
Zur Geologie und Stratigraphie des Kendenggebietes zwischen Trinil und Soerabaja. *Ibid., 3*, 136-149.
DUBOIS, E. 1936
Racial identity of *Homo soloensis* Oppenoorth (including *Homo modjokertensis*, von Koenigswald) and *Sinanthropus pekinensis*, Davidson Black. *Proc. Acad. Sci. Amst. 39*, 1180-1185.
WEIDENREICH, F. 1938
Pithecanthropus and *Sinanthropus*. *Nature 141*, 378-379.
KOENIGSWALD, G. H. R. VON 1940
Neue *Pithecanthropus*-Funde. *Wet. Meded. Dienst. Mijnb. Ned. -O.-Ind. 28*, 1-232.

GRIMM, H. 1940
Untersuchungen über den fossilen Hominidschädel von Modjokerto aus Java. *Anthrop. Anz.* *17*, 254-265.

KOENIGSWALD, G. H. R. VON 1950
Fossil hominids from the Lower Pleistocene of Java. *Proc. Ninth Internat. Geol. Cong., London, 1948. Sect. 9*, 59-61.

MAYR, E. 1950
Taxonomic categories in fossil hominids. *Cold Spring Harbour Symposia on Quantitative Biology 15*, 109-118.

HOOIJER, D. A. 1956
The lower boundary of the Pleistocene in Java and the age of *Pithecanthropus*. *Quarternaria 3*, 5-10.

HOOIJER, D. A. 1962
The Middle Pleistocene fauna of Java. In *Evolution und Hominisation*. Ed. G. Kurth, pp. 108-111. Stuttgart: Gustav Fischer Verlag.

KURTÉN, B. 1962
The relative ages of the australopithecines of Transvaal and the pithecanthropines of Java. *Ibid.*, pp. 74-80.

CAMPBELL, B. 1964
Quantitative taxonomy and human evolution. In *Classification and human evolution*. Ed. S. L. Washburn, pp. 50-74. London: Methuen and Co. Ltd.

The 'Meganthropus' Mandibular Fragments

Fig. 87 The Meganthropus II mandibular fragment
(1941)
Courtesy of Professor G. H. R. von Koenigswald

Synonyms | *Meganthropus palaeojavanicus* (Weidenreich, 1945); *Megan-*
and other names | *thropus* I and II (Robinson, 1953); *Paranthropus palaeojavanicus*
(Robinson, 1954); *Pithecanthropus palaeojavanicus* (Piveteau,
1957)

Site | Sangiran, about 40 miles west of Trinil, near Surakarta, Central
Java, Indonesia.

Found by | G. H. R. von Koenigswald and his assistants, 1939, 1941;
P. Marks, 1953.

Geology | The 1941 fragment was taken from a thick layer of black clay
in the Djetis deposits containing numerous freshwater shells.
This layer, which underlies the Trinil deposits at Sangiran,
had formed the bed of a large Pleistocene lake.

238

The 'Meganthropus' Mandibular Fragments

Associated finds · No artefacts were associated with the find but the fossil fauna included a primitive horned ox (*Leptobos*) and a sabre-toothed cat (*Epimachairodus*); forms typical of the Djetis beds.

Dating · The dating of the Djetis beds has been discussed in relation to the second Sangiran calvarium (*q.v.*). Kurtén (1962) includes the *Meganthropus* specimens in the group that he equates in age with *Australopithecus africanus*, i.e. First Interglacial period (Günz–Mindel or Antepenultimate Interglacial).

Morphology · MANDIBLE

The 1941 specimen consists of part of the right side of the body of a massive hominid mandible that extends from the canine socket to the first molar tooth. Three large teeth are *in situ*, the first and second premolars and the first molar. The jaw is remarkable in size, being larger than any known example from modern man, equalled by few modern gorillas and only exceeded by *Gigantopithecus*. The inner aspect of the fragment bears genial tubercles for the attachment of the extrinsic tongue muscles, and shows part of the digastric impression. There is no simian shelf. The mental foramen is placed about midway between the upper and lower borders of the bone.

TEETH

The first premolar is bicuspid and asymmetrical in occlusal view, and has two well defined grooves on its buccal surface. The second premolar bears two mesial cusps and a talonid basin. The fused ridges joining the cusps separate the anterior and posterior foveae whilst the buccal grooves are feebly represented. The first molar is a robust tooth but attrition has exposed the dentine leaving little of the fissural pattern. The occlusal surface is elongated mesiodistally. Despite the extensive wear it is probable that there were six cusps present.

Dimensions · *Weidenreich* (1945): *Marks* (1953)

MANDIBLES

| Specimens | Body Height at | | | Body Thickness at | | |
	Symphysis	Mental Foramen	M2/M3	Symphysis	Mental Foramen	M2/M3
1939 (cast)	(38·2)	38·5?	30·0?	19·0	19·3	20·3
1941 (cast)	47·0	48·0	45·0	25·5	28·0	26·3
1953	37·0	42·0	47·0	—	—	—

( ) Approximate measurement

239

TEETH

		Lower Teeth (Crown Dimensions)				
Specimens		PM1	PM2	M1	M2	M3
1939 (cast)	l	—	—	13·0	14·1	—
	b	—	—	13·0	14·3	—
1941 (cast)	l	10·0	10·2	15·0	—	—
	b	12·0	12·0	13·5	—	—
1953	l	—	8·5★	14·0★	14·5★	15·5
	b	—	—	13·0	13·0	13·0

★ Damaged

Affinities Although the first fragments were found by von Koenigswald in 1939 and 1941, because of wartime difficulties they were first fully described from casts and named by Weidenreich (1945). Weidenreich believed that they belonged to a hominid who was ancestral to *Pithecanthropus* and thus to modern man, denying any relationship with the australopithecines. This view was taken up vigorously by Robinson (1953) who suggested that *Meganthropus* is at least generically equivalent to *Paranthropus*. Later, in a review of the classification of the australopithecines (Robinson, 1954), *Meganthropus palaeojavanicus* was renamed *Paranthropus palaeojavanicus*. This step was criticized by Remane (1954a and b), rejected by von Koenigswald (1954, 1957), but stoutly defended by Robinson (1955, 1962).

Recently Tobias and von Koenigswald (1964) have compared the Javan *Meganthropus* jaw fragments and the *Homo habilis* type mandible from Bed I, Olduvai Gorge. They commented upon certain dental similarities and drew attention to the lack of a mandibular torus in the *Meganthropus* fragments, contrasting these with known australopithecine mandibles. In their view *H. habilis* in Africa and *Meganthropus* in Java may represent the same grade of hominization within the African and Asian Lower and Early Pleistocene sequence.

In view of this controversy it can be concluded only that there were giant hominid forms in the Far East living sympatrically with early *Homo erectus*. These forms may have been australopithecines or they may represent an earlier less evolved form of *Homo erectus* equivalent to *Homo habilis*.

Original 1941 Specimen, G. H. R. von Koenigswald Collection, 240

Geologisch Instituut, Der Rjksuniversiteit te Utrecht, Utrecht, Netherlands.

Casts The University Museum, University of Pennsylvania, Philadelphia 4, Pennsylvania, U.S.A. (1941 Specimen).

References WEIDENREICH, F. 1945
Giant early man from Java and South China. *Anthrop. Pap. Amer. Mus. 40*, 1-134.

MARKS, P. 1953
Preliminary note on the discovery of a new jaw of *Meganthropus*, von Koenigswald, in the Lower Middle Pleistocene of Sangiran, Central Java. *Indones. J. Nat. Sci. 109*, 26-33.

ROBINSON, J. T. 1953
Meganthropus, australopithecines and hominids. *Am. J. Phys. Anthrop. 11*, 1-38.

KOENIGSWALD, G. H. R. VON 1954
The *Australopithecinae* and *Pithecanthropus*, III. *Proc. Acad. Sci. Amst. 57*, 85-91.

REMANE, A. 1954a
Structure and relationships of *Meganthropus africanus*. *Am. J. Phys. Anthrop. 12*, 123-126.

REMANE, A. 1954b
Methodische Probleme der Hominiden—Phylogenie II. *Z. Morph. Anthrop. 46*, 225-268.

ROBINSON, J. T. 1954
The general and species of the *Australopithecinae*. *Am. J. Phys. Anthrop. 12*, 181-200.

ROBINSON, J. T. 1955
Further remarks on the relationship between *Meganthropus* and australopithecines. *Am. J. Phys. Anthrop. 13*, 429-446.

KOENIGSWALD, G. H. R. VON 1957
Meganthropus and the *Australopithecinae*. *Proc. Third Pan-African Cong. Prehist.,Livingstone, 1955.* Ed. J. D. Clark, pp. 158-160. London: Chatto and Windus.

PIVETEAU, J. 1957
Traité de Paléontologie, VII. Paris: Masson et Cie.

KURTÉN, B. 1962
The relative ages of the australopithecines of Transvaal and the pithecanthropines of Java. In *Evolution und Hominisation.* Ed. G. Kurth, pp. 74-80. Stuttgart: Gustav Fischer Verlag.

ROBINSON, J. T. 1962
The origin and adaptive radiation of the australopithecines. *Ibid.*, pp. 120-140.

The Solo Calvaria and Tibiae

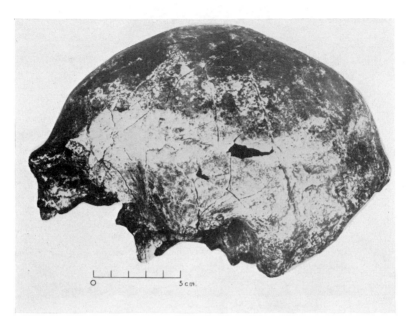

Fig. 88   Solo skull number 6
Left lateral view
Courtesy of Professor J. S. Weiner

Synonyms *Homo (Javanthropus) soloensis* (Oppenoorth, 1932a); *Homo*
and other names *soloensis* (Oppenoorth, 1932b); *Homo primigenius asiaticus*
(Weidenreich, 1933); *Homo neanderthalensis soloensis* (von
Koenigswald, 1934); *Homo sapiens soloensis* (Campbell, 1964)
Solo man; Ngandong man

Site   Ngandong, six miles north of Ngawi, Central Java, Indonesia.

Found by   C. ter Haar, 1931–1933; G. H. R. von Koenigswald, 1933.

Geology   The valley of the river Solo, north of Ngawi, has three
gravel terraces at two metres, seven metres and 20 metres,
where the river has cut through the previous fluviatile deposits.
It was in the high 20-metre terrace, above the Trinil beds,
that the Solo finds were uncovered.

242

Associated finds A few small stone implements were found with the bones as well as some stone balls, but too few indisputable artefacts were recovered to constitute an industry. Several rayfish spines and deer antlers were found, which may have been used as spearpoints or pick-axes. A large quantity of mammalian bones were associated with the hominid remains, mostly belonging to an axis deer (*Cervus javanicus*) or banteng cattle. Other forms included pigs (*Sus terhaari, Sus macrognathus*), rhinoceros (*Rhinoceros sondaicus*), hippopotamus (*Hexaprotodon*

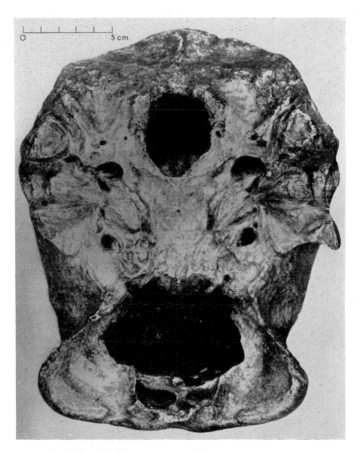

Fig. 89   Solo skull number 11
Basal view
Courtesy of Professor J. S. Weiner

243

ngandongensis) and primitive elephant (*Stegodon sp.*). The diagnostic fossils for the Ngandong fauna are *Cervus javanicus* and *Sus terhaari*.

Dating Assessment of the stratigraphy and fauna suggest that the dating of the Ngandong deposits is Upper Pleistocene (von Koenigswald, 1949).

Morphology CALVARIA

In all eleven calvaria and two tibiae were unearthed at this site. Seven were regarded as being adult on grounds of sutural fusion (Weidenreich, 1951) and, of these, two were believed to be male, two female and the remainder of indeterminate sex.

The calvaria are all thick, several showing signs of injury during life. In profile they all possess the same general form which, in combination with similar dimensions, suggests that they represent a homogeneous population. Particular features of the profile are supra-orbital ridges separated by a central depression, sloping foreheads and strongly marked nuchal crests. The glenoid fossae are deep, and the articular eminences and mastoid processes pronounced. The base of No. 11 is complete apart from its anterior portion.

TIBIAE

Tibia A is broken at both ends, lacking articular surfaces, whereas Tibia B is nearly complete. Both bones are straight and appear modern in form.

Dimensions CALVARIA

Weidenreich (1951)

Max. Lengths 191–221   Max. Breadths 146–159

Cranial Indices 65·2–75·2

(Based on the six best-preserved skulls)

TIBIAE	*Length*
Tibia A	300 (broken)
Tibia B	365

        ★   ★   ★

CALVARIA

Singer (1958)

Measurements taken on the original material.

Max. Lengths 192·5–220·3   Max. Breadths *c.* 144–*c.* 155

Cranial Indices 66·8–76·5

Cranial Lengths, Breadths and Length/Breadth Indices					
Skull No.	1	5	6	9	10	11
Length	196·0	220·3	192·5	c. 201·0	202·6	200·0
Breadth	c. 148·0	c. 147·0	c. 144·0	c. 150·0	c. 155·0	c. 144·0
Cranial Index★	75·6	66·8	75·3	74·6	76·5	72·0

★ Calculated from Singer's figures

Affinities   The calvaria reported by Oppenoorth (1932a) were originally assigned by him to the genus *Homo* and placed in a sub-genus *Javanthropus*. The name was dropped in subsequent publications (Oppenoorth, 1932b, 1937) and the name *Homo soloensis* was proposed. However, Weidenreich (1933) suggested the name *Homo primigenus asiaticus* as part of a wider scheme of hominid classification. Vallois (1935) criticized the creation of a sub-genus for Solo man and suggested that these people were simply a local variety of Neanderthal man. Soon after this there followed a protracted controversy between Dubois and von Koenigswald regarding the relationships of all the Javan finds; Dubois (1936) at first proclaimed the 'racial identity' of Solo man, Modjokerto man and Peking man, but later believed that Solo man was identical with Wadjak man and thus a form of *Homo sapiens* (Dubois, 1940).

However, von Koenigswald had indicated his belief in the Neanderthal affinities of this form by naming it *Homo neanderthalensis soloensis* (von Koenigswald, 1934).

Finally Weidenreich examined all the Solo material in considerable detail and, in an unfinished paper (Weidenreich, 1951), elected not to enter the discussion on nomenclature; he contented himself by stating that 'Ngandong man is not a true Neanderthal type but distinctly more primitive and very close to *Pithecanthropus* and *Sinanthropus*'. None the less, von Koenigswald has adhered to his view that Solo man is a primitive 'tropical Neanderthaler' (von Koenigswald, 1958). In a recent classification of the *Hominidae* it has been proposed to include Solo man as a sub-species of *Homo sapiens* (*Homo sapiens soloensis*) distinct from modern man (*H. sap. sapiens*), Neanderthal man (*H. sap. neanderthalensis*) and Rhodesian man (*H. sap. rhodesiensis*) (Campbell, 1964).

Originals   G. H. R. von Koenigswald Collection, Geologisch Instituut, Der Rijksuniversiteit te Utrecht, Utrecht, Netherlands.

245

Casts   Not available at present.

References   OPPENOORTH, W. F. F. 1932a
Homo (Javanthropus) soloensis, een plistoceene Mensch von Java. *Wet. Meded. Dienst. Mijnb. Ned.-O.-Ind. 20*, 49-75.

OPPENOORTH, W. F. F. 1932b
De vondst paleolithische menschelijke schedels op Java. *De Mijningin-genieur 5*, 106-116.

KOENIGSWALD, G. H. R. VON 1933
Ein neuer Urmensch aus dem Diluvium Javas. *Zbl. Miner., Geol. A und B Paläont.*, 29-42.

WEIDENREICH, F. 1933
Ueber pithekoide Merkmale bei Sinanthropus pekinensis u seine stammesgeschichtliche Beurteilung. *Z. f. Anat. u Entw. Gesch. 99*, 212-253.

KOENIGSWALD, G. H. R. VON 1934
Zur stratigraphie des javanischen Pleistocän. *De Ing. Ned. Ind. 1* 185-201.

VALLOIS, H. 1935
Le *Javanthropus*. *Anthropologie 45*, 71-84.

DUBOIS, E. 1936
Racial identity of *Homo soloensis*, Oppenoorth (including *Homo modjokertensis*, von Koenigswald) and *Sinanthropus pekinensis*, David-son Black. *Proc. Acad. Sci. Amst. 39*, 1180-1185.

OPPENOORTH, W. F. F. 1937
The place of *Homo soloensis* among fossil men. In *Early Man*. Ed. G. G. MacCurdy. pp. 349-360. Philadelphia and New York: J. B. Lippincott.

DUBOIS, E. 1940
The fossil human remains discovered by Dr G. H. R. von Koenigs-wald and attributed by him to *Pithecanthropus erectus*, in reality remains of *Homo wadjakensis* (syn. *Homo soloensis*). *Proc. Acad. Sci. Amst. 43*, 494-496, 842-851, 1268-1275.

KOENIGSWALD, G. H. R. VON 1949
The discovery of early man in Java and Southern China. *Stud. Phys. Anthrop. 1*, 83-98.

WEIDENREICH, F. 1951
Morphology of Solo man. *Anthrop. Pap. Amer. Mus. 43*, 205-290.

KOENIGSWALD, G. H. R. VON 1958
Der Solo-Mensch von Java; ein Tropische Neanderthaler. In *Hundert Jahre Neanderthaler*. Ed. G. H. R. von Koenigswald. pp. 21-26. Utrecht: Kemink en Zoon.

SINGER, R. 1958
Ibid., p. 22.

CAMPBELL, B. 1964
Quantitative taxonomy and human evolution. In *Classification and human evolution*. Ed. S. L. Washburn. pp. 50-74. London: Methuen and Co. Ltd.

The Wadjak Skulls

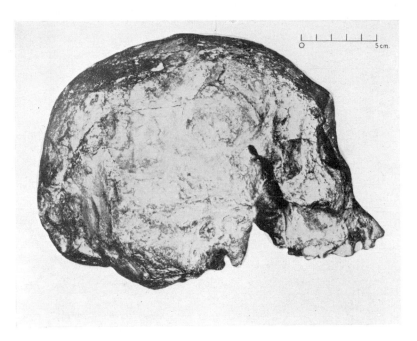

Fig. 90   Wadjak I skull
Right lateral view
Courtesy of Professor J. S. Weiner

Synonyms and other names	*Homo wadjakensis* (Dubois, 1921); *Homo sapiens wadjakensis* (Pinkley, 1936) Wadjak man
Site	Near Tulungagung, Central Java, Indonesia.
Found by	B. D. Van Rietschoten, 1889.
Geology	The skulls were found cemented in a limestone breccia terrace near an ancient lake.
Associated finds	No implements or other artefacts were associated with the skulls and the fossil fauna does not differ significantly from that found in modern Java.
Dating	In view of the degree of mineralization of the skulls and the modern fauna, the earliest possible dating is probably late Pleistocene.

247

Morphology The remains comprise a nearly complete skull and a broken mandible (Wadjak I), with a nearly complete mandible and a broken skull (Wadjak II). In addition there were some isolated teeth, and fragmentary bones.

SKULLS

The skulls are heavily mineralized and dolichocephalic. Wadjak I, apparently not fully prepared, was considered to be female by Dubois, whilst Wadjak II was believed to be male. Both skulls are large with well filled brain cases. The vault of Wadjak I is keeled with prominent superciliary ridges and a receding forehead; the occiput is protuberant, tending towards the formation of a bun.

The facial skeleton shows depression of the root of the nose, flattening of the nasal bones and a low position of the orbits. The maxillae present a marked degree of alveolar prognathism.

MANDIBLES

The mandibles are large and heavily built, the Wadjak II specimen bearing a definite chin.

TEETH

The Wadjak teeth are large but fall within the size range of modern Australian aboriginals. The upper molar size sequence is modern, $M1 > M2 > M3$. The bite is edge to edge, there being neither overbite nor overjet in occlusion.

Molar Cusp Pattern
(Lower Molars)

	$M1$	$M2$
Wadjak I	Y5	+4
Wadjak II	Y5	+4

Dimensions Dubois (1922)

WADJAK I SKULL

Max. Length 200   Max. Breadth 145
Cranial Index 72·5 (Dolichocephalic)
Cranial Capacity 1,550 cc

WADJAK II SKULL

Cranial Capacity 1,650 cc

Affinities In the original description, published many years after the   248 discovery of the material, Dubois (1922) drew attention to the Australoid features of Wadjak man, but elected to define a new species *Homo wadjakensis*. In a subsequent assessment, Pinkley (1936) suggested that this was unjustified and identified Wadjak man with *Homo sapiens*. This step has never been seriously contested and the Australoid affinities of Wadjak man have been widely accepted.

Originals   Collection Dubois, Rijksmuseum von Natuurlijke Historie, Leiden, Netherlands.

Casts   The University Museum, University of Pennsylvania, Philadelphia 4, Pennsylvania, U.S.A.

References   DUBOIS, E. 1922
The Proto-Australian fossil man of Wadjak, Java. *Proc. Acad. Sci. Amst. 23*, 1013–1051.
PINKLEY, G. 1936
The significance of Wadjak man, a fossil *Homo sapiens* from Java. *Peking nat. Hist. Bull. 10*, 183–200.

CHINA   CHOUKOUTIEN (LOWER CAVE)

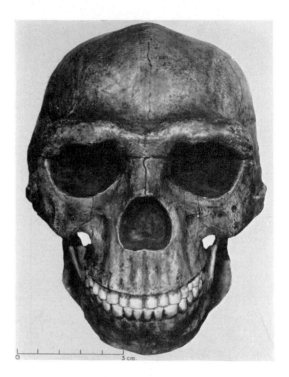

Fig. 91   The Peking adult female skull (cast)
Restored by F. Weidenreich
Frontal view
*Courtesy of the Trustees of the British Museum
(Nat. Hist.)*

Synonyms — Homo sp. (Zdansky, 1927); *Sinanthropus pekinensis* (Black,
and other names — 1927); *Pithecanthropus pekinensis* (Boule and Vallois, 1952);
Pithecanthropus sinensis (Piveteau, 1957); *Homo erectus pekinensis*
(Weidenreich, 1940; Campbell, 1964); *?Sinanthropus lanti-
anensis* (Woo, 1964)
Pekin man; Peking man

Site — Near the village of Choukoutien, 25 miles south-west of
Peking, Peoples' Republic of China.

Found by — J. G. Anderson, 1921; O. Zdansky, 1923; B. Bohlin, 1927;   250

The Peking 'Lower Cave' Remains

W. C. Pei and the Cenozoic Research Laboratory, 1928–1937; J. K. Woo, 1959 and 1964.

Geology　The hills near Choukoutien are formed from Silurian limestone which has been undermined and eroded by percolating ground waters producing caves and fissures. At Locality 1 a huge cavern roof has collapsed on top of the cave-filling, which is made of red clays and fallen rocks consolidated into a calcareous breccia. The cliff face at the principal site is 150 feet deep and was divided by Davidson Black into 15 sections each of ten feet, lettered A–O from above downwards. It was in this cave-filling, at various levels, that much of the material was found.

Associated finds　The tools found at Locality 1 belong to a crude 'Chopper-tool' industry, and were made from imported coarse-grained quartz and greenstone. They are in the form of a few cores and numerous flakes which were probably utilized.

The remains of an extensive mammalian fauna was recovered with Peking man. Amongst the forms recognized were some insectivores, bats and lagomorphs, numerous rodents, some small and large carnivores, a large deer (*Megaloceros pachyosteus*) and rhinoceros. A new faunal list has been given by Kahlke (1962). At this site also were found ash heaps and pieces of charcoal; the charcoal, although of no use for radiocarbon dating on account of its age, provides the first clear evidence of the use of fire by early man.

Dating　The usually accepted dating of the Choukoutien site, in view of the fauna, is Middle Pleistocene. By a combination of pollen and faunal analysis, Kurtén (1959) suggested that the dating equivalent of the Choukoutien deposits should be sought in the European glaciations and not in an interglacial, in his view probably the Second Glaciation (Elster II, Mindel II or the Antepenultimate Glaciation). The age of this glaciation, according to Evernden, Curtis and Kistler (1958) using the potassium–argon method, is 370,000 B.P. (a figure which may be revised to *c.* 400,000 B.P.). This is an appropriate date for the Choukoutien deposits but is dependent upon Kurtén's correlation. In a recent assessment of the geology of the cave-filling (Huang, 1960), it has been suggested that the deposits were laid down over a long period as six successive

251

gravel beds; the basal layer during the First Glaciation, the lower two layers during the First Interglacial, and the upper three layers during the Second Glaciation. This correlation is rejected by Kahlke (1962), as were a previous Cromerian correlation and a Mindel–Riss Interglacial correlation proposed on palaeontological grounds.

Morphology The hominid remains from Choukoutien, which were described in a remarkable series of monographs by Black and Weidenreich, consist of 14 calvaria and 11 mandibles in varying states of preservation, as well as numerous teeth and a few post-cranial bones.

A new mandible has been attributed to Peking man by Woo and Chao (1949) and a second mandible (Woo, 1964) has been

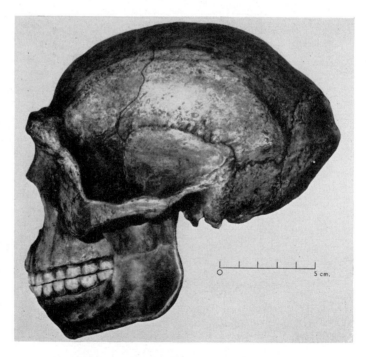

Fig. 92 The Peking adult female skull (cast)
Restored by F. Weidenreich
Left lateral view
Courtesy of the Trustees of the British Museum (Nat. Hist.)

recovered from Lantian, Shensi Province, and named *Pithe-canthropus lantianensis.*

CALVARIA

The first calvarium to be found, now known as Skull III, was recovered from Locus E. It is well preserved but the face and base are missing. The braincase is characterized by a flattened but keeled frontal region with a pronounced supra-orbital visor, a well marked post-orbital constriction and a prominent occipital torus. The mandibular fossae are deep and narrow. In frontal view the side walls of the cranium slope inwards towards the apex so that the maximum width lies in the region of the temporal bone above the small mastoid process—a feature not found in modern man. This particular skull was described by Black (1931) as being adolescent; later Weidenreich (1943) considered it to be juvenile. The principal morphological features of the remaining calvaria are similar to those of Skull III but tend to be more coarsely represented.

MANDIBLES

Three of the best-preserved mandibles have been recon-structed by Weidenreich (1936). These show the recession of the symphysial region, the narrow but rounded dental arcade, thickening of the body of the mandible inside the alveolar margin (mandibular torus), the presence of genial tubercles for the tongue muscles and an unusually large bicondylar breadth. A point of detail is the high incidence of multiple mental foramina (cf. Heidelberg jaw). The new mandible (1959) has a narrow alveolar arch, a moderate mandibular torus and four mental foramina on the right side.

TEETH

In total 147 teeth were examined by Weidenreich (1937), 83 socketed, 64 isolated. Out of the 132 (52 upper, 82 lower) permanent teeth present, every tooth was represented but only lower deciduous teeth are known. This collection is believed to come from 32 individuals, 20 of whom were adolescent or adult and 12 children. Five more teeth have been reported, but not described, by Woo (1960).

The most striking feature of the teeth is their variability in size, the range of which has permitted their division into two main groups believed to represent males and females. In

253

general the teeth are robust and characteristically wrinkled. The upper incisors are shovel-shaped and frequently have a well developed basal tubercle with finger-like processes directed toward the free margin of the tooth. The upper canines are large and project beyond the occlusal line whilst the lower canines are smaller and tend to form cutting edges, thus resembling incisors. There is no trace of a diastema and the premolars are non-sectorial. In almost all of the canines, premolars and molars there is a cingulum which in the case of the molars has traces of stylid cusps. The cusp pattern is basically dryopithecine with a tendency towards transformation into the 'plus' pattern by reduction of the metaconid. The first and second permanent molars are of approximately the same size, but the third molar tends to be smaller than either. The permanent molars, premolars and milk molars display a degree of enlargement of the pulp cavity (taurodontism).

The eruption order of the teeth of Peking man differs from that of modern man in that the second permanent molar arises before both premolars and canine.

POST-CRANIAL BONES

The femora of Peking man are represented by seven fragments of shaft, none with an articular surface. Woo (1960) reported new limb material—'two fragments of humerus and tibia'. The tibial fragment is said to have an even smaller medullary cavity than the femora. The femora are unusual in the thickness of the cortical bone, the antero-posterior flattening of the shaft and the poor development of the *linea aspera*. The remains of the upper limb consist of two fragments of humerus, a broken clavicle and a lunate bone. The pieces of humerus have no articular surface, but are thick-walled and one has a strong deltoid impression. The clavicle is slender and well curved but bears strong muscular markings. The lunate belongs to the right side and is small by comparison with that of modern man. The bone is somewhat eroded having lost part of its dorsal surface, part of the semi-lunar facet for the scaphoid and the apex of the ridge joining the radial and triquetral surfaces. These scanty remains of the limbs do not appear to differ widely from the corresponding bones in modern man.

254

Dimensions CALVARIA
Locus E. Skull III (Black, 1931)
Length (glabella/occipital) 187·6   Max. Parietal Breadth 133·0
Cranial Index 73·5
   (Dolichocephalic)
Cranial Capacity 915 cc
   (Weidenreich)
CRANIA
Weidenreich (1943)
Max. Length range 188–199
Max. Breadth range 137·2–143
Cranial Index range 71·4–72·6 (Dolichocephalic)
Cranial Capacity (5 skulls) range 915 cc–1,225 cc
MANDIBLES G1♂ and H1♀
Reconstructed by Weidenreich (1936)

| | | | | | At Mental Foramen | |
No.	Length	Bicondylar Breadth	Symphysial Height	Ramus Height	Height	Thick- ness
G1 ♂	103·0*	146·4*	40·0*	66·7	34·0	16·4
H1 ♀	94·0*	101·8*	31·5	59·0	26·0	15·4

* Restored.

The differences between these measurements were taken as
evidence of sexual dimorphism.

Sinanthropus lantianensis (Woo, 1964)

No.	Height at Mental Foramen	Symphysial Height	Thickness at M1
P.A.102	27·0	35·0	16·0

TEETH
Weidenreich (1937)

| | Permanent Dentition (Crown Dimension Ranges) | |
Upper Teeth	Length	Breadth
Central Incisors (I1)	9·8–10·8	7·5– 8·1
Lateral Incisors (I2)	8·2– 8·3	8·0– 8·2
Canines (C)	8·5–10·5	9·8–10·6
First Premolars (PM1)	7·4– 9·2	10·5–12·8
Second Premolars (PM2)	7·2– 8·9	10·3–12·5
First Molars (M1)	10·0–13·1	11·7–13·7
Second Molars (M2)	10·2–12·2	12·2–13·4
Third Molars (M3)	8·7–10·4	10·4–12·5

Lower Teeth	Length	Breadth
Central Incisors (I1)	6·0– 6·8	5·8– 6·8
Lateral Incisors (I2)	6·3– 7·2	6·4– 7·3
Canines (C)	8·1– 9·0	8·2–10·4
First Premolars (PM1)	7·9– 9·8	9·1–10·8
Second Premolars (PM2)	8·2– 9·2	8·0–11·1
First Molars (M1)	9·9–13·6	10·1–12·8
Second Molars (M2)	11·3–13·1	11·1–12·9
Third Molars (M3)	10·0–13·8	10·0–12·4

	Deciduous Dentition (Crown Dimensions)	
Lower Teeth	Length	Height
Central Incisors (DI1)	4·3	3·6
Lateral Incisors (DI2)	—	—
Canines (DC)	6·1–6·2	5·2– 5·3
First Molars (DM1)	9·8	8·4–10·1

POST-CRANIAL BONES

Weidenreich (1941)

Lunate: Length (prox./dist. diam.) 14·5
      Breadth (radio/ulnar diam.) 14·4
      Height (dorso/volar) 16·5

Clavicle: Length (145)
        Circumference 34 (Mid-point)

Humerus: Angle of Torsion 137°
        Length (324)

Femora: Lengths (400–407)
       Mid-shaft Widths 29·2–29·7
       Mid-shaft Depths 22·8–27·1

( ) Estimated measurement

Affinities Initially the name *Sinanthropus pekinensis*, conferred by David-son Black (1927), referred solely to the hominid molar tooth upon which the genus was founded. It was not long before Black's bold step was apparently justified by the subsequent finds, but soon afterwards the resemblances between *Pithe-canthropus* and *Sinanthropus* began to become clear (Boule, 1929). Later, when the Choukoutien material had been fully studied by Weidenreich, he took the view that the differences between *Pithecanthropus* and *Sinanthropus* were of a racial character only. It has been suggested that Peking man, in company with several other Middle Pleistocene hominids, should be classified under the name of *Homo erectus* (Mayr, 1950) and given the geographic subspecific designation *pekinensis*. This proposal has been incorporated in a classification agreed at a recent conference (Campbell, 1964).

Originals All of the early material, except one lower premolar and one upper molar, was lost during the 1939–45 war. Fortunately most of the bones had been cast and studied intensively by Weidenreich. The two teeth are at the University of Uppsala, Sweden. The newer material is kept at The Institute of Vertebrate Palaeontology and Palaeoanthropology, Academia Sinica, Peking, Peoples' Republic of China.

Casts The University Museum, University of Pennsylvania, Philadelphia 4, Pennsylvania, U.S.A.

References ZDANSKY, O. 1927
Preliminary notice on two teeth of a hominid from a cave in Chihli (China). *Bull. geol. Soc. China.* 5, 281–284.
BLACK, D. 1927
On a lower molar hominid tooth from the Chou Kou Tien deposit. *Palaeont. sinica*, Ser. D, 7, 1–29.
BOULE, M. 1929
Le *Sinanthropus. Anthropologie 39*, 455–460.
BLACK, D. 1931
On an adolescent skull of *Sinanthropus pekinensis* in comparison with an adult skull of the same species and with other hominid skulls, recent and fossil. *Palaeont. sinica*, Ser. D, 7, II, 1–145.
WEIDENREICH, F. 1936
The mandibles of *Sinanthropus pekinensis*: a comparative study. *Palaeont. sinica*, Ser. D, 7, III, 1–163.
WEIDENREICH, F. 1937
The dentition of *Sinanthropus pekinensis*: a comparative odontography of the hominids. *Palaeont. sinica*, New Ser. D, 1, 1–180, 1–121 (plates).
WEIDENREICH, F. 1940
Some problems dealing with ancient man. *Amer. Anthrop. 42*, 375–383.
WEIDENREICH, F. 1941
The extremity bones of *Sinanthropus pekinensis. Palaeont. sinica*, New Ser. D, 5, 1–150.
WEIDENREICH, F. 1943
The skull of *Sinanthropus pekinensis*; a comparative study on a primitive hominid skull. *Palaeont. sinica*, New Ser. D, 10, 1–291.
BOULE, M., and VALLOIS, H. V. 1946
Les hommes fossiles. 3rd Ed., p. 122. Paris: Masson et Cie.

MAYR, E. 1950
Taxonomic categories in fossil hominids. *Cold Spring Harbour Symposia on Quantitative Biology 15*, 109-118.
PIVETEAU, J. 1957
Traité de Paléontologie VII, p. 384. Paris: Masson et Cie.
KURTÉN, B. 1959
New evidence on the age of Pekin man. *Vertebrata Palasiatica 3*, 173-175.
WOO, J. K., and CHAO, T. K. 1959
New discovery of *Sinanthropus* mandible from Choukoutien. *Vertebrata Palasiatica 3*, 169-172.
HUANG, W. P. 1960
Restudy of the Choukoutien *Sinanthropus* deposits. *Vertebrata Palasiatica 4*, 45-46.
HUANG, W. P. 1960
On the age of basal gravel of Choukoutien *Sinanthropus* site and of the 'Upper gravel' and 'Lower gravel' of the Choukoutien region. *Ibid.*, 4, 47-48.
WOO, J. K. 1960
The unbalanced development of the physical features of *Sinanthropus pekinensis* and its interpretation. *Vertebrata Palasiatica 4*, 17-26.
KAHLKE, H. D. VON 1962
Zur relativen Chronologie ostasiatischer Mittelpleistozän-Faunen und Hominoidea-Funde. In *Evolution und Hominisation*. Ed. G. Kurth. pp. 84-107. Stuttgart: Gustav Fischer Verlag.
WOO, J. K. 1964
A newly discovered mandible of the Sinanthropus type—*Sinanthropus lantianensis*. *Scientia Sinica 13*, 801-811.

The Peking 'Upper Cave' Remains

CHINA   CHOUKOUTIEN (UPPER CAVE)

<table>
<tr><td>Synonyms and other names</td><td>Homo sapiens (Pei, 1934)
Pekin Upper Cave man; Peking Upper Cave man</td></tr>
<tr><td>Found by</td><td>W. C. Pei, 1930.</td></tr>
<tr><td>Site</td><td>Near the village of Choukoutien, 25 miles south-west of Peking, Peoples' Republic of China.</td></tr>
<tr><td>Geology</td><td>Above the Choukoutien red earth beds, in the Silurian limestone, a cave was found separated from the fissure containing the remains of Sinanthropus. The upper cave was filled with grey loam and calcite mixed with pieces of the collapsing roof. Five layers of deposits were distinguished.</td></tr>
<tr><td>Associated finds</td><td>An extensive fossil fauna was uncovered with the human bones, as well as some stone tools and ornamental objects. The fauna included bear (Ursus spelaeus), red deer (Cervus elaphus), Sika deer (Pseudaxis hortulorum), hyena (Crocuta ultima), several carnivores, an ostrich (Struthio sp.) and numerous hares.
A few flint and quartz tools were found in the cave-filling, also some bone needles, polished deer antlers, marine shells and fish bones, perforated fox and deer teeth, painted stones and polished beads.</td></tr>
<tr><td>Dating</td><td>The fauna indicates that the deposits date from the Upper Pleistocene period, possibly the final phase of the Fourth Glaciation (Würm or Last Glaciation) or even post-glacial times (Coon, 1963).</td></tr>
<tr><td>Morphology</td><td>Bones from at least seven individuals were found in the Upper Cave, including three crania, several mandibles and parts of mandibles, a right maxilla bearing teeth, a right patella, a right first metatarsal, an upper third of radius and the shaft of a right femur lacking both ends.</td></tr>
</table>

CRANIA

Cranium No. 101 is that of an elderly male, Nos. 102 and 103 those of younger women. All three are dolichocephalic but have low vaults.

MANDIBLES

Mandibles 101, 104, 108 and 109, two complete and two fragmentary, have well marked chins and No. 101 has a mandibular torus. The mental foramina are single. Recently it has been suggested that skull No. 102 and mandible No. 104 represent different individuals, thus the total number of the Upper Cave population on the basis of the skulls and mandibles may be eight instead of seven (Wu, 1961).

POST-CRANIAL BONES

Those illustrated by Wu do not appear to differ appreciably from those of modern man.

Dimensions   Weidenreich (1939)

Skull No.	Max. Length	Max. Breadth	Cranial Index	Cranial Capacity
101	204	143	70·2	c. 1,500
102	196	(136)	69·3	c. 1,380
103	184	131	71·1	c. 1,290

( ) Estimated

Affinities   Weidenreich (1939) believed that the crania represented early forms of modern man and saw racial features relating to Mongoloid, Melanesoid and Eskimoid groups, but Wu (1961) concluded that Upper Cave man 'represents the primitive Mongoloid type and is closely related to the ancestors of modern Chinese, Eskimo and Amerindians, though there remain some typical Mongolian characters not yet well developed'. Coon (1963) also believed that the skulls belonged to the Mongoloid race. He suggested that the dolichocephaly of the female skulls is due to distortion.

Originals   The originals were lost during the 1939–45 war. The recent study by Wu (1961) was based upon casts.

Casts   The University Museum, University of Pennsylvania, Philadelphia 4, Pennsylvania, U.S.A. (Crania only)

References   PEI, W. C. 1934
A preliminary report on the Late-Palaeolithic cave of Choukoutien. *Bull. geol. Soc. China 13*, 327-358.
PEI, W. C. 1939
On the Upper Cave industry. *Peking nat. Hist. Bull. 13*, 175-179.
PEI, W. C. 1939
The Upper Cave industry of Choukoutien. *Palaeont. sinica*, New Ser. D, *9*, 1-56.
WEIDENREICH, F. 1939
On the earliest representatives of modern mankind recovered on the soil of East Asia. *Peking nat. Hist. Bull. 13*, 161-174.

WU, X. Z. 1961
Study on the Upper Cave man of Choukoutien. *Vertebrata Palasiatica*
3, 202–211.
COON, C. S. 1963
The origin of races, pp. 472–475. London: Jonathan Cape.

The 'Gigantopithecus' Teeth

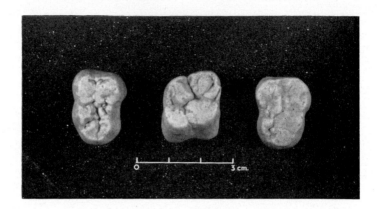

Fig. 93   *Gigantothropus* teeth
Left—Left third lower molar, occlusal view
Cast specimen 4
Centre—Right second upper molar, occlusal view
Cast specimen 3
Right—Right third lower molar, occlusal view
Cast specimen 1, type specimen

Synonyms and other names   *Gigantopithecus blacki* (von Koenigswald, 1935); *Giganthropus blacki* (Weidenreich, 1945; Weinert, 1948)

Sites   (*a*) Chinese pharmacies in Hong Kong, Canton and elsewhere. (*b*) Leng-Chai-Shan, Liu-Cheng, Central Kwangsi, South China.

Found by   *G. H. R. von Koenigswald*
1935 Hong Kong, No. 1. Right third lower molar.
1935 Hong Kong, No. 2. Right third lower molar.
1935 Canton, No. 3. Right second upper molar.
1939 Hong Kong, No. 4. Left third lower molar.
In addition two other teeth were found which may belong to *Gigantopithecus*, namely one right upper central incisor and one upper canine.

W. C. Pei
1956. 47 teeth from pharmacies; three isolated teeth *in situ* in a cave deposit (Ta-Hsin); two mandibles and 12 isolated teeth from another cave in Kwangsi, Southern China.

1957–1958. A further mandible of enormous size was discovered in the same cave.

Geology Since the actual site of recovery of the 'drugstore' fossils is unknown, their geology is bound to be uncertain. Yellow earth adherent to some of the teeth has suggested that they came from cave or fissure deposits. Von Koenigswald was told that the fossils came from the provinces of Kwangsi and Kwantung, Southern China. The recent finds have come from limestone caves in Kwangsi. The fossils were contained in the cave deposit, covered by hard breccia and a stalagmitic crust.

Associated finds The pharmacists' stocks of fossils included the teeth of orang (*Pongo*), giant panda (*Ailuropoda*), tapir (*Tapirus*), bear (*Ursus*), rhinoceros (*Rhinoceros*) and primitive elephant (*Stegodon*). A fauna collectively known as the 'Ailuropoda-orang' fauna of Southern China.

The fossil bones recovered with the new mandibles confirm that *Gigantopithecus* formed a part of this fauna.

Dating The 'Ailuropoda-orang' fauna of Southern China is regarded as being of early Middle Pleistocene age.

Morphology 'DRUGSTORE' TEETH
The material found by von Koenigswald consists of one upper and three lower molar teeth derived from at least two separate sites, and belonging to at least four individuals. Specimens 1, 2 and 3 have no roots, but tooth 4 has a stout,

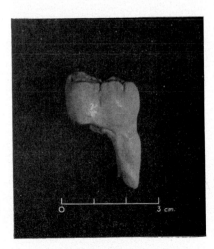

Fig. 94 *Gigantothropus* tooth
Left third lower molar, buccal view
Cast specimen 4

grooved posterior root. Each tooth shows some degree of flat occlusal wear. The crowns of the teeth are high (hypsodontism) and slab-sided, bearing blunt but tall cusps arranged in the dryopithecine pattern. The furrows separating the six cusps and accessory cusps are narrow and deep. Some secondary enamel wrinkling is present in the lower molars. The pulp cavities are not enlarged.

KWANGSI MANDIBLES AND TEETH

The first mandible is well preserved and only the portions behind the second molars are missing on both sides. Twelve teeth are still in place but two were broken during excavation. The mandible is very robust having an elongated dental arcade and a sloping symphysial region buttressed internally by what appears to be a simian shelf. The teeth are very worn and appear small; on these grounds the mandible has been attributed to an elderly female. The incisors are relatively small and the canines resemble incisors, unlike the conical canines of the great apes. There is a small diastema between the canine and the first premolar on the left; the first premolars are moderately sectorial in shape whilst the second premolars are somewhat molariform. The molars are too worn to allow a description of the cusp pattern.

The second mandible is young with unerupted permanent canines. The premolars are molariform. The second molars are larger than the first and bear six cusps, whereas the first molars are a little worn and appear five-cusped. The isolated teeth included representatives of the upper premolars and molars, probably of both sexes.

The third mandible was recovered from the same cave deposit as the other two specimens. It is enormous. The teeth are little larger than those previously known but the mandible is unbelievably robust. There is a diastema between the lower canines and the first premolar, a stout simian shelf and marked wear on the posterior aspect of the canine which suggests interlocking of the eye teeth. All of these features are pongid rather than hominid.

Dimensions   TEETH

von Koenigswald (1952)

It is apparent, from these measurements, that these are very robust teeth, unequalled in size by those of man or apes, fossil   264 or recent. For instance although the teeth of '*Zinjanthropus*' (*q.v.*) are very large, the second upper molar (length 17, breadth 21) only approaches the dimensions of the corresponding *Gigantopithecus* tooth.

Tooth No.	Third lower molars			Second upper molar
	1	2	4	3
Crown length	22·3	23·1	22·4	18·7
Crown breadth	18·5	17·5	17·3	27·3
Crown height	(11·2)	(11·8)	(12·8)	(15·0)

( ) Estimated measurement

MANDIBLES
Pei and Li (1958)

	Mandibular Height			Mandibular Thickness		
	At I1	PM2	M2	At I1	PM2	M2
Mandible 1	66·1	58·7	—	36·6	31·5	?38·6
Mandible 2	71·3	53·1	—	39·1	33·5	—
Mandible 3	101·5	79·9	76·3	47·0	36·0	37·0

TEETH
Pei and Li (1958)

	Length I1–M2	Length PM1–M2	Length M1–M3	Crown Dimensions M3 ($l \times b$)
Mandible 1	85·1	65·4	—	20·0 × 16·2
Mandible 2	95·8	74·5	—	—
Mandible 3	101·3	73·8	59·2	21·9 × 17·5

Affinities The type specimen (Tooth No. 1) was described by von Koenigswald (1935) and named *Gigantopithecus blacki*, since he believed it to belong to a new giant anthropoid. Subsequently casts of the teeth were examined by Weidenreich, who emphasized the hominid features and saw in this form the forerunner of the other Far Eastern hominids, *Pithecanthropus* and *Sinanthropus* (Weidenreich, 1945). The hominid status of *Gigantopithecus* was supported by Weinert (1950), but not by Remane (1950) who regarded the outline of the lower molars as simian. Meanwhile, Hooijer (1949) asserted that the question of the status of *Gigantopithecus* could not be settled until either a premolar or a canine were known.

After the war von Koenigswald (1952) published a full description of the type specimen and the other molars, as well as some referred material; in this work he stated that '*Gigantopithecus* probably was the latest survivor of an Asiatic stock which more or less parallels the human line', but he would not accept *Gigantopithecus* as an australopithecine *sensu stricto*. Later it became known that much more material had been found in China (Pei, 1957; Pei and Woo, 1956) including a fossil mandible with twelve teeth *in situ* (the Kwangsi jaw) and later still second and third specimens. Von Koenigswald (1958) has reviewed the position in the light of the new material and accepts the hominid features of the new teeth. Pei and Woo (1956) suggested that *Gigantopithecus* belonged to a side branch of the anthropoids but von Koenigswald was prepared to go farther and placed these forms in a 'pre- or parahominid' group equivalent to the *Australopithecinae*.

In a review of the status of *Gigantopithecus*, Dart (1960) said that this form 'like the zinjanthropine variation upon the australopithecine theme has carried its range of human dental variation well beyond the anthropoid limits'.

Originals   (1) G. H. R. von Koenigswald Collection, Geologisch Instituut, Der Rijksuniversiteit te Utrecht, Utrecht, Netherlands.
(2) The Institute of Vertebrate Palaeontology and Palaeoanthropology, Academia Sinica, Peking, Peoples' Republic of China.

Casts   The University Museum, University of Pennsylvania, Philadelphia 4, Pennsylvania, U.S.A. (Von Koenigswald's specimens)

References   KOENIGSWALD, G. H. R. VON 1935
Eine fossile Säugetierfauna mit Simia aus Südchina. *Proc. Acad. Sci. Amst. 38*, 872–879.
WEIDENREICH, F. 1945
Giant early man from Java and South China. *Anthrop. Pap. Amer. Mus. 40*, 1–134.
WEINERT, H. 1948
Die Riesen—Affenmenschen und ihre stammesgeschichtliche Bedeutung. Munich: Rudolph Muller und Steinicke.
HOOIJER, D. A. 1949
Some notes on the *Gigantopithecus* question. *Am. J. Phys. Anthrop. 7*, 513–518.

WEINERT, H. 1950
Über die neuen Vor- und Fruhmenschenfunde aus Afrika, Java, China und Frankreich. *Z. Morph. Anthr. 42*, 113-148.

REMANE, A. 1950
Bemerkungen über *Gigantopithecus blacki*. In Weinert, H. *Ibid., 42*, 134-137.

KOENIGSWALD, G. H. R. VON 1952
Gigantopithecus blacki von Koenigswald, a giant fossil hominoid from the Pleistocene of Southern China. *Am. J. Phys. Anthrop. 43*, 295-325.

PEI, W. C., and WOO, J. K. 1956
New materials of *Gigantopithecus* teeth from South China. *Acta Palaeont. sin. 4*, 489-490.

PEI, W. C. 1957
Discovery of *Gigantopithecus* mandible and other material in Liu-Cheng district of Central Kwangsi in South China. *Vertebrata Palasiatica 1*, 65-72.

KOENIGSWALD, G. H. R. VON 1958
Gigantopithecus and *Australopithecus*. *The Leech (Johannesburg) 28* 101-105.

PEI, W. C., and LI, Y. H. 1958
Discovery of a third mandible of *Gigantopithecus* in Liu-Cheng, Kwangsi, South China. *Vertebrata Palasiatica 2*, 198-200.

DART, R. A. 1960
The status of *Gigantopithecus*. *Anthrop. Anz. 24*, 139-145.

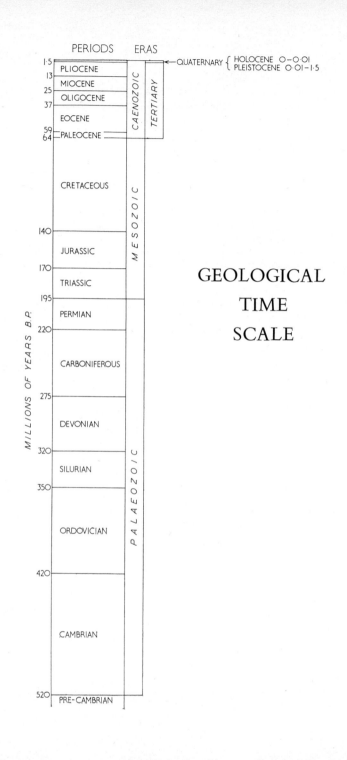

PERIODS   ERAS

1·5 ──────────────────────── ←── QUATERNARY { HOLOCENE 0 – 0·01
     PLIOCENE   PLEISTOCENE 0·01 – 1·5
13
     MIOCENE   C
25   A
     OLIGOCENE   E
37   N
                       O
     EOCENE   Z   TERTIARY
                       O
59   I
64   PALEOCENE   C

     CRETACEOUS   M
                       E
                       S
140   O
                       Z
     JURASSIC   O
                       I
170   C
     TRIASSIC
195
     PERMIAN
220
     CARBONIFEROUS

275

     DEVONIAN

320   P
     SILURIAN   A
350   L
                       A
                       E
     ORDOVICIAN   O
                       Z
                       O
420   I
                       C

     CAMBRIAN

520
     PRE-CAMBRIAN

MILLIONS OF YEARS B.P.

GEOLOGICAL

TIME

SCALE

GLOSSARY

Glossary

ACHEULEAN
A stone tool culture characterized by distinctive pointed or almond-shaped hand-axes. Type site, St Acheul, Amiens (Somme), Northern France.

ALVEOLAR PROGNATHISM
Forward projection of the portions of the jaws that bear teeth.

ANGLE OF THE CRANIAL BASE
The angle between the basi-occiput and the body of the sphenoid.

APPENDICULAR SKELETON
The bones of the limbs and the limb girdles.

ARTEFACTS (ARTIFACTS)
Man-made objects.

ARTESIAN WATER
Ground water contained under pressure.

ARTIODACTYLA
The zoological name given to an order of ungulates. The 'even-toed' ungulates, e.g. deer, antelopes, gazelle, buffalo, pigs, oxen, sheep and goats.

ASTERION
A point on the skull at which the lambdoid, parieto-mastoid and occipital sutures meet.

ATLANTHROPUS
The generic name given to a group of North African Middle Pleistocene hominids. After the Atlas range of mountains, North Africa.

AURIGNACIAN
A culture of stone, bone and antler which includes flint side and end scrapers, spear tips and blades. The bone implements include awls and spear points. The culture is associated with the Cro-Magnon people. Type site; Aurignac, Haute Garonne, France.

AUSTRALOPITHECINAE
The zoological sub-family which contains the fossil 'ape-men', 'man-apes' and 'near men'.

AUSTRALOPITHECINE
(*n.*) A member of the zoological sub-family *Australopithecinae*.
(*adj.*) Pertaining to the zoological sub-family *Australopithecinae*.

AUSTRALOPITHECUS
The generic name given to a group of South and East African Lower Pleistocene hominids. 'Southern ape.'

AXIAL SKELETON
The skull, vertebral column and thorax.

b
Breadth.

BASALT
Fine-grained extrusive igneous rock of dark colour, low in silica.

BENTONITIC CLAY
A clay formed from decomposed volcanic ash.

BICUSPID
(*n.*) A premolar tooth.
(*adj.*) Two-cusped.

BIPEDAL GAIT
Two-legged walking.

B.P.
Before present.

BRACHYCEPHALIC
Having a Cranial Index above 80. 'Broad-headed.'

BRECCIA
Sedimentary rock composed of angular fragments of derived material embedded in a finer cement.

BREGMA
The point at which the coronal and sagittal sutures of the skull meet.

BURIN
An Upper Palaeolithic chisel-like stone tool suitable for engraving bone, wood, horn or soft stone.

271

Glossary

CAENOZOIC (CENOZOIC)
See geological time scale.

CALCITE
The stable crystalline form of calcium carbonate at normal temperatures, hence the commonest mineral form of limestone.

CALCRETE
Desert soil cemented with calcium carbonate.

CALOTTE
The bones of the cranial vault.

CALVARIUM
A skull which has lost the bones of the face including the mandible.

CAMBRIAN
See geological time scale.

CARABELLI'S CUSP
An accessory cusp on the lingual surface of the crown of an upper molar tooth.

CARABELLI'S PIT AND GROOVES
Features found on the lingual surface of the crown of an upper molar tooth.

CATARRHINE MONKEYS
A sub-group of the order Primates which includes monkeys from Africa and Asia. 'Old-world monkeys.'

CHERT
A siliceous rock found in limestone of which flint is an example.

CHIGNON
An occipital 'bun-like' protuberance of the skull characteristic of the Neanderthalers of the Fourth Glaciation.

CINGULUM
A collar-like ridge of enamel around the base of the crown of a tooth.

CLACTONIAN
A primitive flake culture found in Europe which includes concave scrapers, cores and some flakes with retouched edges. Type site, Clacton-on-Sea, Essex.

CONGLOMERATE
Sedimentary rock composed of rounded pebbles of older rocks embedded in a younger cement, e.g. puddingstone.

CRANIAL INDEX
$$\frac{\text{Max. Cranial Breadth}}{\text{Max. Cranial Length}} \times 100$$

CRANIUM
That part of the skull forming the brain-case.

CRASSIDENS
The specific name given to a group of South African hominids known from Swartkrans. 'Big-toothed.'

CYPHANTHROPUS
The generic name formerly given to Rhodesian man. 'Stooping-man.'

DENTAL CARIES
A pathological process, with destruction of tooth enamel and dentine, leading to infection and loss of the tooth.

DEVONIAN
See geological time scale.

DIABASE
An American term for dolorite. A medium-grained dark igneous rock, low in silica.

DIASTEMA
A gap between the teeth.

DIOPSIDE
A colourless or pale green mineral of calcium magnesium silicate.

DOLICHOCEPHALIC
Having a Cranial Index of less than 75. 'Long-headed.'

DOLOMITE
1. Mineral calcium magnesium carbonate.
2. Limestone containing more than 50% mineral dolomite.

DRIPSTONE
Crystalline calcium carbonate deposited from water in layers or strata.

DRYOPITHECINE
(*n.*) A member of the genus *Dryo-pithecus.*
(*adj.*) Pertaining to the genus *Dryo-pithecus.*

DRYOPITHECUS
The generic name given to a group of Middle Miocene apes. 'Oak-ape.'

ENAMEL WRINKLING
Secondary folding of the enamel of the occlusal surface of a tooth; consistently found in the molar teeth of the modern orang-utan (*Pongo*), also known in australopithecine and pithecanthropine teeth.

ENDOCAST
A cast of a cavity, displaying internal surface features in relief.

FAUNAL BREAK
A sudden change in the character of the fossil fauna encountered during excavation of successive layers of a deposit; possibly due to partial erosion and subsequent redeposition of later material containing a different fauna, or to faunal migration.

FAURESMITH
A Palaeolithic stone tool culture found in South Africa consisting of hand-axes and cleavers. Type site, Faure-smith, Orange Free State, Republic of South Africa.

FELSPAR (FELDSPAR)
A group of crystalline minerals con-sisting of silicates of aluminium with sodium, potassium, barium or calcium. Decomposition of felspars produces clays.

FEMORO-CONDYLAR ANGLE
The angle between the shaft of the femur and a line drawn tangentially to the articular surfaces of the femoral condyles.

FERRICRETE
Soil cemented with iron oxide.

FLUVIATILE DEPOSITS
Deposits produced by river action.

FRANKFURT PLANE
An agreed plane in which skulls may be oriented for comparative purposes. Arranged horizontally, it passes through the lower orbital margin and forms a tangent to the upper margin of the external auditory meatus.

HABILIS
The specific name given to a group of East African Lower Pleistocene homi-nids. 'Able, handy, vigorous, mentally skilful.'

HOLOCENE
See geological time scale.

HOMINID
(*n.*) A member of the zoological family *Hominidae.*
(*adj.*) Pertaining to the zoological family *Hominidae.*

HOMINIDAE
The zoological family which includes fossil and modern man as well as the fossil 'ape-men', 'man-apes' and 'near-men'.

HOMININAE
The zoological sub-family which con-tains fossil and modern man.

HOMININE
(*n.*) A member of the zoological sub-family *Homininae.*
(*adj.*) Pertaining to the zoological sub-family *Homininae.*

HOMINOID
(*n.*) A member of the zoological super-family *Hominoidea.*
(*adj.*) Pertaining to the zoological super-family *Hominoidea.*

HOMINOIDEA
The zoological super-family which contains fossil apes, 'ape-men', 'man-apes', 'near-men' and men, as well as modern great apes and modern man.

273

T<small>FM</small>

Glossary

HOMO
The generic name given to the group of hominids which contains fossil and modern man.

HYPSODONT
Having teeth with tall crowns, e.g. the horse.

ILMENITE
Mineral iron titanium oxide.

INION
A position on the skull marked by the external occipital protuberance.

INTERGLACIAL
A warm period between two major glaciations.

INTERPLUVIAL
A dry phase between two rainy periods.

INTERSTADIAL
A warm interval within a major glaciation.

JAVANTHROPUS
The sub-generic name formerly given to a group of hominids from Ngandong, Java. 'Java-man.'

KARSTIC CAVES
Caves formed in limestone by the action of water.

Length.

LAMBDA
A point on the skull at which the sagittal and lambdoid sutures meet.

LEVALLOISIAN
A Palaeolithic flake tool culture produced by striking serviceable flakes from a prepared core; recognized in Europe, Asia and Africa. Type site, Levallois-Perret, Paris.

LIAS (LIASSIC)
A rock formation consisting of layers of limestone, marl and clay attributed to the Lower Jurassic period. ? Corruption of 'layers'.

LISSOIR
A polishing or rubbing tool.

LOAM
An iron-rich mixture of clay and silt.

LOESS
A fine-grained deposit of wind-blown material.

MAMELON
A small hillock or tuberosity; small elevations found along the free margin of a newly erupted incisor tooth.

MEGANTHROPUS
The generic name given to a group of early hominids from Java and East Africa. 'Big-man.'

MESOCEPHALIC (MESATICEPHALIC)
Having a Cranial Index which lies between 75-80. 'Middle-headed.'

MESOZOIC
See geological time scale.

MOUSTERIAN
A stone tool culture consisting of side scrapers, disc cores and points widely represented in Europe, North Africa and Western Asia; frequently associated with Neanderthal remains. Type site, Le Moustier, Peyzac, Dordogne, France.

NUCHAL
Pertaining to the nape of the neck.

OBSIDIAN
Volcanic glass, capable of fine conchoidal fracture producing sharp flakes.

OCCLUSAL SURFACE
The biting surface of a tooth.

OLDOWAN
An Early Palaeolithic stone tool culture consisting of crudely made cutting, scraping or chopping implements produced by flaking stones in two directions. Type site, Olduvai Gorge, Tanzania, East Africa.

Glossary

ORTHOGNATHOUS
Without forward projection of either upper or lower jaw. 'Straight-jawed.'

OSTEOARTHRITIS
A degenerative disease of joints characterized by pain, swelling and deformation.

OSTEODONTOKERATIC
Pertaining to bone, tooth and horn.

OVERBITE
The degree of vertical overlap of the incisor teeth in occlusion.

OVERJET
The degree of separation of the upper and lower incisor teeth in the horizontal plane when the teeth are occluded.

PALAEOZOIC
See geological time scale.

PALYNOLOGY
The study of pollen

PARANTHROPUS
A generic name given to a group of South African Pleistocene hominids. 'Beside or equal-to-man.'

PEARSON'S FORMULA
Female Cranial Capacity = 0·000,375 × Length × Breadth × Height + 296·4.
Male Cranial Capacity = 0·000,365 × Length × Breadth × Height − 359·34.

PERISSODACTYLA
The zoological name given to an order of ungulates. The 'odd-toed' ungulates, e.g. equids, rhinoceroses and tapirs.

PITHECANTHROPINE
(*n.*) A member of the genus *Pithecanthropus*.
(*adj.*) Pertaining to a member of the genus *Pithecanthropus*. Frequently used colloquially when referring to hominids of the *Homo erectus* group.

PITHECANTHROPUS
The generic name given to a group of Asian Middle Pleistocene hominids. 'Ape-man.'
(Members of this genus are commonly

TFM*

included within the genus *Homo* by modern taxonomists.)

PLESIANTHROPUS
The generic name given to a group of South African Lower Pleistocene hominids. 'Near-man.'

PLUVIAL
A rainy period.

POLYPHYLETIC
Concerning, or derived from several ancestral forms.

PONGID
(*n.*) A member of the zoological family *Pongidae*.
(*adj.*) Pertaining to the zoological family *Pongidae*.

PONGIDAE
The zoological family which contains both fossil and modern great apes.

PROGNATHOUS
Forward projection of the jaws.

PROMETHEUS
The specific name given to a group of Transvaal Lower Pleistocene hominids in the mistaken belief that their remains were associated with evidence of fire.

QUADRITUBERCULATE
Bearing four tubercles.

QUARTZITE
A siliceous metamorphic rock consisting of quartz grains, or minute quartz crystals, set in a quartz cement.

RACLOIRS
Mousterian side scrapers.

ROBUSTICITY INDEX
An index obtained by expressing the thickness of a bone in terms of its length.

SECTORIAL TEETH
Teeth having a cutting edge and a scissor-like action in occlusion.

SEPSIS
Bacterial infection with the formation of pus.

Glossary

SESAMOID
A bone formed within a tendon.

SHOVELLED INCISORS
Incisor teeth that are scooped out on their lingual surfaces and having a variable degree of inrolling of their lateral borders.

SILCRETE
Soil cemented with silica.

SIMIAN SHELF
A buttress of bone that reinforces the symphysial region of the mandible in monkeys and apes.

SINANTHROPUS
The generic name formerly given to a group of Middle Pleistocene hominids found near Peking, Peoples' Republic of China. 'Chinese-man.'

SKULL
The bony skeleton of the head, including the lower jaw. The term is not always strictly applied.

STALACTITE
A conical or irregular deposit of calcite hanging from the roof of a cave; formed by precipitation of calcium carbonate from drops of lime-saturated water.

STRATIGRAPHY
A branch of geology concerned with the formation, constituents and sequence of stratified deposits.

STILLBAY
A Late Palaeolithic stone tool culture found in South Africa consisting of finely made blades and weapon heads. Type site, Stillbay, Cape Province, Republic of South Africa.

SUPERCILIARY RIDGES
Smoothly rounded ridges of bone found on the frontal region of the skull above the position of the eyebrows.

SYLVIAN CREST
A ridge found on the internal surface of the parietal bone of some primitive hominid skulls; it occupies the Sylvian fissure of the brain.

SYMPATRIC
Two or more animal populations that occupy the same habitat but do not interbreed are termed sympatric.

SYMPHYSIAL ANGLE
(SYMPHYSEAL ANGLE)
The angle made by the principal dimension of the mandibular symphysis and the lower border of the body of the mandible.

TAURODONT
Teeth having enlarged pulp cavities. 'Bull-toothed.'

TAYACIAN
A rather poorly defined flake culture, allied to the Clactonian, found in Europe and the Near East. Type site, Tayac, Les Eyzies, Dordogne, France.

TEKTITES
Glassy objects of supposed extra-terrestrial origin.

TELANTHROPUS
The generic name given to a group of South African hominids known from Swartkrans. ?'Distant-man' or 'Perfect-man.'

TORUS
A smooth rounded protuberance.

TRAVERTINE
Almost pure calcium carbonate rock deposited around lime-rich springs and lakes.

TROPICAL SAVANNAH
Tropical grassland containing scattered trees, such as the Baobab in Africa.

TUFA
A calcareous deposit, usually spongy in texture formed near lime-rich springs and rivers.

TUFF
A consolidated deposit of volcanic ash often laid down in water.

276

Glossary

VILLAFRANCHIAN
1. A faunal assemblage containing new types of mammals such as *Elephas* (*Archidiskodon*), *Equus*, *Bos* (*Leptobos*) and *Camelus*, which appeared suddenly during the Lower Pleistocene. Type site, Villafrancha d'Asti, Italy.

2. Pertaining to the Lower Pleistocene.

ZINJANTHROPUS
The generic name given to an East African Lower Pleistocene hominid. 'East African man.'

INDEX

Index

Main references to fossil hominids are in **bold type.** References to charts, diagrams and tables are in *italics*

Index

Index

pigs, var.: 199
Piltdown man: 10
pithecanthropines: *13*, 67, 169
Pithecanthropus: 73, 109, 138, 150, 226, 227, 229, 232, 236, 240, 245, 256, 265
Pithecanthropus I: 221, 223, 228, 230
Pithecanthropus II: 226, 228, 230
Pithecanthropus IV: 229, 232
Pithecanthropus B: 232
Pithecanthropus capensis: 185
Pithecanthropus erectus: 221, 222, 227, 229
Pithecanthropus lantianensis: 253
Pithecanthropus modjokertensis: 229, 232, 234, 235, 236
Pithecanthropus palaeojavanicus: 238
Pithecanthropus pekinensis: 250
Pithecanthropus robustus: 229, 232
Pithecanthropus sinensis: 250
platycnemia: 49
Pleistocene lake and river deposits: 96, 101, 120, 145, 149, 226, 234, 238, 247
Pleistocene period (general): 3–4, 5, 8, *13*, 14, 70, 96, 101, 107, 120, 137, 145, 149, 179, 216, 221, 226, 234, 238, *268*
   Lower (early), 96, 146, 149, 163, 170, 199, 222, 230, 235
   Middle, 96, 101, 111, 138, 149, 179, 187, 222, 227, 230, 235, 244, 251, 263
   Upper (late), 39, 44, 49, 50, 154, 212, 215, 222, 247, 259
Pleistocene sands and gravels: 70, 101, 107
'Ples, Mrs': 171
Plesianthropus 5: 168, 200
Plesianthropus transvaalensis: 168, 207
Pliocene period: 179, *268*
Pluvial and interpluvial periods (phases): 3–4, *4*
Pluvials, North African: 108, 114
point tools: 8, 10, 11, 76, 90, 96
pollen dating: 31, 215, 251
polyphyletic theory (of racial origin): 158
Pongo: 263
Post-glacial period (phase): *4*
Potamochoerops antiquus: 178, 186
Potamochoerus majus: 138
Potamochoerus sp.: 120
potassium-argon dating: 12, 14, 66, 120, 138, 154, 222, 230, 235, 251
'Praesapiens' (term): 54
Praesapiens man: 52
Pre-Cambrian dolomitic limestone: 169, 178, 186
Pre-Cambrian period: *268*
premolars: 21, 24, 39, 57, 66, 67–8, 72, 78, 86, 104, 106, 108, 111, 112, 114–*15*, 135, 146, 171, 172, 179, 180, 187, 188, 189, 193, 201, 239, 240, 255–6
Presentation scheme for fossil hominids: 28
'Pre-Zinjanthropus': 125, 135
'Pre-Zinjanthropus' remains (Olduvai): **125–34**

primates, var.: 120, 138
Proamblysomus antiquus: 178
proboscideans: 96
Procavia antiqua: 169, 178, 186
Procavia capensis: 163
Procavia transvaalensis: 163, 169, 178, 186
prognathism: 49, 72, 90, 111, 149, 164, 180, 200, 216, 230, 248
Promesochoerus sp.: 120
Protomys campbelli: 163
Proto-Stillbay culture: 154
Pseudaxis hortulorum: 259
Pseudhomo: 66
pterygoids: 66
pyorrhoea: 92

quartzites: 107
Quaternary era and period: *268*

Rabat man: 110
Rabat mandible: **110–13**
racloirs (scraper tools, *q.v.*): 90
radii: *20*, 39, 40, 62, 79, 86, 87, 93, 94, 187, 193, 199, 259
radiometric dating: *see* carbon 14 *and* potassium-argon
ramus breadths and widths: 58, 68, 79, 105, 175, 194, 204
ramus heights: 68, 105, 194, 195, 204
rami: *19*, 58, 66, 68, 86, 104, 105, 114, 115, 128, 164, 171, 201
Rangifer tarandus: 39, 48
Recent period: *see* Holocene period
reptiles, var.: 120
Rhenanthropus: 65
Rhinoceros: 263
Rhinoceros sondaicus: 222, 243
rhinoceros, var.: 96, 138, 251
Rhinolophus cf. capensis: 163, 199
Rhodesian man (*Homo sapiens rhodesiensis*, *q.v.*): 35, 73, **153–60**, 213, 245
Rhodesian skull: 138, 153, 155, 158, 212
ribs: 39, 62, 79, 170
ridges:
   brow, 34, 122, 138, 155, 179, 222
   superciliary, 49, 216, 248
   supra-orbital, 44, 62, 77, 171, 188, 212, 244
Riss I and II glacial periods (phases): *4*, 5, *13*, 57, 108
Riss-Würm interglacial period (phase): *4*, 5, *13*, 53, 57, 71, 77, 84, 90
robusticity indices: 108, 112, 115, 195 (*see also under names*)
rocks suitable for tool-making: 7
rodents, var.: 120, 169, 178, 199, 215, 251

Sacra: *19*, 154, 157, 171, 174–5
Saldanha man: *13*, 158, 211, 213
Saldanha skull (calvarium): 138, 158, **211–14**

287

Index

Index